A New
Certificate Arithmetic

Revision Books

'O' LEVEL TESTS IN ARITHMETIC
C. C. T. Baker
5s.; *with answers* 7s. 6d.

'O' LEVEL TESTS IN ALGEBRA
J. Hislop
4s. 6d.; *with answers* 7s. 6d.

A New
Certificate Arithmetic

JAMES HISLOP, M.A. B.Sc.
Hamilton Academy

VOLUME I

METHUEN & CO LTD
36 ESSEX STREET · LONDON · WC2

First published May 16th 1957
Reprinted 1959

1.2

Catalogue No 8133/u (Without Answers)
8135/u (With Answers)

PRINTED IN GREAT BRITAIN
BY BUTLER AND TANNER LTD, FROME

Contents

Preface

The contents of this volume should provide adequate material for the first half of a 3–4 year Arithmetic course in any type of secondary school. Herein the pupil is introduced to certain fundamental topics and to others such as Area, Proportional Division, Profit and Loss, Simple Interest, etc., which are further developed in the second volume.

Care has been taken (i) to reduce textual material to a minimum; (ii) to give adequate, illustrative worked examples; and (iii) to provide sufficient 'drill' material to encourage the less able and problem questions to challenge the more able pupil.

Throughout I have had before me the Mathematical Association Report, the influence of which may be reflected in certain of the methods recommended. Some attention has been given to neglected topics like Significant Figures, Approximation to a certain degree of accuracy, use of Square Root tables, etc., the study of which will be of interest.

My former colleague, James McCall, M.A., made a number of useful suggestions when this volume was in the early manuscript stage. Since then my present colleagues, Robert McKendrick, M.A., B.Sc., and John A. B. Smith, M.A., have been constantly at my elbow and have given valuable assistance in a variety of ways, particularly in checking the answers to the many examples that are a feature of this book. To all of these gentlemen I am deeply grateful and desire here to place that fact on record. I have also to acknowledge my indebtedness to Messrs Macmillan & Co Ltd for permission to reproduce the Square Root tables that appear in this book.

As this volume goes forth I trust it will commend itself to a wide circle of my fellow teachers and that its use may stimulate both the teaching and the learning of the processes of Arithmetic.

J. H.

November 1956

Introductory History

The development of our present number system from very primitive beginnings is a subject of absorbing interest. Only a brief summary can be given here, but the bibliography on page 12 will furnish greater detail.

Number Systems

Basis 2. Probably the most primitive of such systems is that having 2 as its basis. This has been found:

(1) among natives of Queensland who count 'one; two; two and one; two twos; much'.

(2) among African pygmies who count 'one; two; two-one; two-two; two-two-one'.

(3) in the symbols of early Syriac notation; thus: ١ ٢ ٢١ ٢٢
$$\quad\quad\quad\quad\quad\quad 1 \quad 2 \quad 3 \quad 4$$

Basis 3. Natives of Tasmania, a tribe of Tierra del Fuego and the Demaras of Africa appear to have used 3 as the basis of their system. And all numbers beyond 3 were grouped as 'many'.

Basis 4. Certain South American tribes built up their number system with basis 4.

Basis 5, 10. It is fairly certain that the system of 10 was derived from man's acquaintance with his ten fingers. If it is by chance that we have 10 fingers, then it is a very happy chance considered in the light of our number system. And one wonders if it is an indication of the origin of things that many children and adults still appear to have a strong inclination to counting on their fingers.

Basis 20. It is rather astonishing to find a Mexican civilization of an early date using 20 as basis for its number system. Doubtless this was suggested by the totality of 10 fingers and 10 toes.

9

Number Writing

Early Man. When early man recorded the birth of a lamb in his flock by making a scratch on the wall, he had begun number writing. The birth of another lamb necessitated the placing of another scratch by the side of the first, and he had now written 2.

I	II	III
1	2	3

Babylonian (3500 B.C.). The Babylonians, using a wedge-shaped implement to make an impression on a soft clay tablet, varied the position of the wedge to represent different things. Held one way, the wedge made 'unit' impressions, and held at right-angles to this 'tens' impressions were made. A stroke, too, was used to indicate 0.

Egyptian. About this time the Egyptians had produced their own method of number representation, and in particular had symbols for a hundred and a thousand.

Hebrew and Greek. It is rather strange that the Greeks in particular advanced no further than to join the Hebrews in the use of their respective alphabets for number representation. This frequently gave rise to confusion and difficulty.

α	β	ι	κ	ε	εθ
1	2	10	20	60	69

Roman. This system may have been developed in the first instance from the position of the fingers

$$\text{I} \quad \text{II} \quad \text{III} \quad \text{IIII}$$

V (5) may have been derived from the gap between the thumb and forefinger.

IV, VI, etc., came after this.

X (10) may be the two lines crossing out ten individual unit lines.

C (100). The original symbol '⌐' gradually developed to C.

L (50). As the lower half of the 100 symbol '⌐' representation of 50 by L is obvious.

M (1000). Initially the Greek letter Φ representing 1,000 was used and this changed as follows: $\Phi \rightarrow (I) \rightarrow \cap \rightarrow M$.

D (500). This being half of 1,000 developed similarly

$$I) \rightarrow I\supset \rightarrow D$$

Hindu. Our modern method of representation has probably come to us from the Hindu.

About 200 B.C. a well-defined system was in general use, and by A.D. 200 it had been improved very considerably to include all the numbers from 1 to 9. The Hindus, too, used a dot to represent zero, then a polygon, and finally 0.

Arabian. Profiting by the Hindu number writing systems in the tenth and eleventh centuries, the Arabs perfected that system which in the intervening centuries has come to have general acceptance.

Arithmetical Processes

Hitherto all work had been done on the **abacus,** which was a kind of counting-table which enabled one to perform simple additions and subtractions, using concrete material, frequently beads on a wire frame.

The Arabs were the first to attempt arithmetical operations, using the new system. This enabled them to dispense with concrete material and to perform addition and subtraction, using only the abstract numbers. Great difficulty was experienced, however, with multiplication and division, and the latter was not mastered till the fourteenth century in Italy.

A limited knowledge of vulgar fractions is found among the Egyptians and Greeks, but methods of dealing with them are different from ours.

Our decimal notation was developed in the sixteenth century, and in the seventeenth century with the introduction of most of the symbols now used to denote arithmetical operations we were ready to move forward.

Conclusion

Arithmetic, in its most primitive form, goes back to the earliest haunts of humanity, and in its development touches almost every land of the ancient and modern world over a period of more than 5,000 years. And, if it is true that 'Mathematics is the Queen of

Sciences', then it is equally true that 'Arithmetic is the Queen of Mathematics'.

BIBLIOGRAPHY

1. *Mathematics for the Million.* L. Hogben. (Allen & Unwin)
2. *Makers of Mathematics.* A. Hooper. (Faber & Faber)
3. *History of Mathematics.* D. E. Smith. (Ginn & Co.)
4. *Men of Mathematics.* E. T. Bell. (Gollancz)

1

A Revision Chapter

MONEY

(a) **Addition**

	1. £	s.	d.		2. £	s.	d.		3. £	s.	d.
	15	6	7		25	14	3		37	17	$5\frac{1}{2}$
	9	17	4		17	9	11		48	12	$3\frac{1}{4}$
	7	12	10		8	17	6		26	15	7
	17	9	9		13	5	7		53	10	$9\frac{3}{4}$

	4. £	s.	d.		5. £	s.	d.		6. £	s.	d.
	76	11	$7\frac{3}{4}$		256	0	$5\frac{1}{2}$		531	19	$11\frac{1}{4}$
	59	13	2		367	17	$9\frac{1}{4}$		498	13	$8\frac{3}{4}$
	87	9	$10\frac{1}{2}$		473	10	$7\frac{1}{4}$		623	12	$7\frac{1}{2}$
	61	15	$8\frac{1}{2}$		218	13	$6\frac{3}{4}$		714	7	$10\frac{1}{4}$

Find the sum of:

7. £37 16s. $7\frac{1}{2}d$.;   £54 10s. $0\frac{3}{4}d$.;
   £76 15s. 3d.;   £43 8s. $4\frac{1}{4}d$.;

8. £143 12s. $2\frac{1}{4}d$.;   £254 13s. $3\frac{1}{2}d$.;
   £367 15s. $2\frac{3}{4}d$.;   £431 0s. $10\frac{1}{2}d$.

Add together:

9. £700 5s. $0\frac{3}{4}d$.;   £263 4s. $11\frac{1}{2}d$.
   £526 15s. $0\frac{1}{2}d$.;   £299 14s. $11\frac{1}{4}d$.

10. £518 12s. $11\frac{1}{4}d$.;   £431 5s. $2\frac{3}{4}d$.
    £368 14s. $9\frac{1}{4}d$.;   £481 7s. $0\frac{3}{4}d$.

(b) Subtraction

11.	£	s.	d.	12.	£	s.	d.	13.	£	s.	d.
	57	17	$9\frac{1}{2}$		89	15	$6\frac{1}{4}$		75	12	$0\frac{1}{2}$
	38	12	$7\frac{1}{4}$		54	9	$8\frac{3}{4}$		48	15	$2\frac{3}{4}$

14.	£	s.	d.	15.	£	s.	d.	16.	£	s.	d.
	143	16	$3\frac{3}{4}$		256	0	$8\frac{1}{2}$		573	13	$3\frac{1}{4}$
	89	12	$9\frac{1}{2}$		197	5	$6\frac{3}{4}$		395	17	$10\frac{1}{2}$

17. Take £35 10s. $6\frac{1}{4}d.$ from £43 15s. $3\frac{1}{2}d.$

18. From £136 12s. $8\frac{3}{4}d.$ take £97 13s. $10\frac{1}{4}d.$

19. By how much is £243 9s. $6\frac{1}{2}d.$ greater than £176 10s. $3\frac{3}{4}d.$?

20. Find the difference between £356 13s. $9\frac{1}{2}d.$ and £443 8s. $10\frac{3}{4}d.$

21. From the sum of £28 10s. $6\frac{1}{2}d.$ and £43 0s. $10\frac{3}{4}d.$ subtract £67 13s. $5\frac{1}{4}d.$

22. Subtract the sum of £257 12s. $8\frac{1}{4}d.$ and £356 17s. $6\frac{1}{2}d.$ from £800.

23. Which is the greater and by how much:

(i) the sum of £356 10s. $11\frac{1}{2}d.$ and £467 17s. $6\frac{1}{4}d.$

or (ii) the difference between £1,000 and £101 0s. $10d.$?

24. The difference between £543 6s. $8\frac{1}{4}d.$ and £732 17s. $6d.$ is the same as the sum of £43 15s. $0\frac{3}{4}d.$ and another sum of money. Find this sum of money.

25. When the sum of £36 10s. $3\frac{1}{4}d.$, £53 14s. $8\frac{1}{2}d.$, £49 17s. $6\frac{3}{4}d.$ is added to a certain other sum the answer is £157 0s. $11d.$ Find this other sum.

(c) Multiplication

26.	£	s.	d.	27.	£	s.	d.	28.	£	s.	d.
	6	12	$3\frac{1}{2}$		13	17	$5\frac{3}{4}$		76	14	$7\frac{1}{4}$
			$\times 13$				$\times 34$				$\times 46$

29.	£	s.	d.	30.	£	s.	d.	31.	£	s.	d.
	89	10	$0\frac{1}{2}$		167	11	$3\frac{1}{4}$		307	17	$5\frac{3}{4}$
			$\times 59$				$\times 74$				$\times 97$

(d) Division

32. Divide £86 9s. 9½d. by 23
33. „ £456 4s. 4¼d. by 37
34. „ £1,995 3s. 5¾d. by 53
35. „ £3,621 19s. 8¾d. by 167

Using factors:

36. Divide £706 19s. 9d. by 18
37. „ £572 4s. 6d. by 24
38. „ £630 16s. 6d. by 36
39. „ £1,362 14s. 0¾d. by 63
40. „ £1,652 5s. 3d. by 84

(e) Reduction

41. Reduce to pennies,   £72 13s. 6d.
42. „   „   „   ,   £123 15s. 11d.
43. „   „ halfpennies, £326 12s. 9½d.
44. „   „ farthings,   £423 16s. 4¼d.
45. „   „   „   , £547 17s. 6¾d.
46. Reduce to £ s. d.,   17,543 pennies
47. „   „   „ ,   54,631 halfpennies
48. „   „   „ ,   76,395 halfpennies
49. „   „   „ ,   83,793 farthings
50. „   „   „ ,   94,821   „

(f) Miscellaneous

51. Find the sum in £. s. d. of 630 farthings, 852 halfpence, 624 pence and 234 threepences.

52. One bag contains £13 5s. 7½d. in halfpennies and another bag contains £70 18s. 9d. in threepences. Which bag contains the greater number of coins and by how many?

53. Express in £. s. d. the sum of 47 half-crowns, 63 florins, 57 shillings, 139 sixpences and 273 threepences.

54. When the boxes on a certain Flag Day were emptied the following was the result:

   3,501 halfpennies;   7,643 pennies;   1,845 threepences;
   1,043 sixpences;   738 shillings;   325 florins;
                  198 half-crowns

Find in £. s. d. the total value of the collection.

55. A gardener buys 25 plants at 3s. 5d. each and offers a £5 note in payment. How much change does he get? How many packets of seed at 2s. 11d. each could he buy with this change?

56. A sum of £257 16s. 11d. is to be divided equally among 19 people. How much will each person receive?

57. If 45 articles can be bought for £39 7s. 6d., what is the cost of each article? How many can be bought for the same money if each article costs 5s. less?

58. Charity collections for the first six months of a year were £16 7s. 3d., £15 8s. 7d., £17 2s. 1d., £14 16s. 5d., £14 13s. 4d. and £15 4s. 4d. The total sum was divided equally between a number of institutions and each received £7 4s. How many institutions were there?

59. An article can be bought for cash at £5 17s. 6d. or for 14s. 3d. down payment followed by 11 monthly payments of 11s. 3d. each. Which is the cheaper method and by how much?

60. An increase from 4s. $4\frac{1}{2}d$. to 4s. $7\frac{1}{2}d$. in the cost of a gallon of petrol raised the cost of a journey by 1s. $10\frac{1}{2}d$. Find the number of gallons of petrol used on the journey. If the car does 22 miles to the gallon, find the length of the journey.

Exercise 1b

WEIGHT

(a) Addition

1. tons	cwt.	qr.		2. tons	cwt.	st.		3. tons	cwt.	qr.	st.
7	15	1		13	12	7		37	10	0	1
9	11	3		17	14	5		43	8	3	0
8	7	2		24	9	3		56	17	2	0
5	19	1		19	16	6		61	13	3	1

4. cwt.	qr.	lb.		5. cwt.	st.	lb.		6. cwt.	qr.	st.	lb.
5	3	14		17	0	11		14	3	0	6
3	0	17		13	6	13		16	0	1	10
6	2	21		9	5	9		10	2	1	12
2	1	19		15	7	7		18	1	0	8

7. tons	cwt.	qr.	lb.	oz.	**8.** tons	cwt.	st.	lb.	oz.
17	13	0	22	9	27	14	1	11	10
23	16	3	15	13	13	15	6	8	14
31	10	1	25	11	41	12	2	13	12
49	11	2	17	8	56	17	7	9	9

Find the sum of:

9. 5 tons 13 cwt. 2 qr. 17 lb.; 7 tons 3 qr. 20 lb.; 17 cwt. 1 qr. 13 lb.; and 3 tons 10 cwt. 1 qr.

10. 14 tons 2 st. 9 lb.; 9 tons 17 cwt. 11 lb.; 13 cwt. 5 st. 10 lb.; and 17 tons 10 cwt. 7 st.

Add together:

11. 13 tons 6 cwt. 17 lb. 8 oz.; 13 cwt. 3 qr. 10 lb. 12 oz.; 26 tons 2 qr. 3 oz.; 15 tons 17 cwt. 1 qr. 9 oz.

12. 17 cwt. 7 st. 13 oz.; 10 tons 3 st. 13 lb. 5 oz.; 11 tons 12 cwt. 9 lb. 11 oz.; 9 tons 17 cwt. 5 st. 7 lb.; and 16 tons 3 st. 12 oz.

(b) Subtraction

13. tons	cwt.	qr.	**14.** tons	cwt.	st.	**15.** tons	cwt.	qr.	lb.
9	13	1	17	11	4	26	12	2	13
6	16	3	13	17	7	19	15	3	22

16. tons	cwt.	st.	lb.	**17.** tons	cwt.	qr.	lb.	oz.
35	19	5	9	29	13	1	11	13
26	17	7	12	21	16	2	17	9

18. tons	cwt.	st.	lb.	oz.
76	12	7	9	9
48	17	3	10	12

19. From 23 tons 3 qr. 21 lb. 7 oz. subtract 17 tons 11 cwt. 2 qr. 10 oz.

20. Take 21 tons 17 cwt. 10 lb. 8 oz. from 25 tons 3 st. 7 lb. 3 oz.

2

21. By how much is 3 tons 13 cwt. 2 qr. 7 oz. greater than 2 tons 17 cwt. 3 qr. 17 lb. 9 oz.?

22. Which is the greater: 12 tons 17 cwt. 1 qr. 7 lb. 13 oz. *or* 12 tons 16 cwt. 7 st. 13 lb. 5 oz., and by how much?

23. Subtract the sum of 3 tons 11 cwt. 5 lb. and 5 tons 7 cwt. 1 qr. 12 oz. from 10 tons.

24. From the sum of 7 tons 9 cwt. 17 lb. 3 oz. and 12 tons 1 qr. 12 lb. 7 oz. subtract 15 tons 5 cwt. 3 qr. 12 oz.

25. From the difference of 12 tons 17 cwt. 3 qr. 11 oz. and 17 tons 1 st. 12 lb. 7 oz. take the sum of 2 tons 1 qr. 23 lb. 9 oz. and 17 cwt. 6 st. 13 oz.

(c) Multiplication

26. tons	cwt.	qr.	lb.	oz.
3	14	3	21	9
				×43

27. tons	cwt.	st.	lb.	oz.
5	9	5	13	11
				×67

28. tons	cwt.	qr.	st.	lb.	oz.
13	17	1	1	9	13
					×79

(d) Division

29. Divide 95 tons 2 cwt. 1 qr. 17 lb. 2 oz. by 37

30. Divide 217 tons 11 cwt. 4 st. 8 lb. 14 oz. by 59

Using factors:

31. Divide 103 tons 13 cwt. 3 qr. 14 lb. by 32

32. Divide 162 tons 8 cwt. 3 lb. 8 oz. by 56

33. Divide 121 tons 6 cwt. 2 lb. 8 oz. by 72

(e) Reduction

34. Reduce to lb.: 7 tons 13 cwt. 2 qr. 23 lb.

35. „   „ lb.: 13 tons 7 cwt. 5 st. 12 lb.

36. „   „ oz.: 3 tons 17 cwt. 15 lb. 12 oz.

37. „   „ oz.: 17 tons 15 cwt. 7 st. 9 oz.

38. Reduce to tons, cwt., st., lb.: 7,563 lb.

39. „   „ tons, cwt., qr., lb., oz.: 79,438 oz.

40. „   „ tons, cwt., st., lb., oz.: 83,576 oz.

(f) Miscellaneous

41. A grocer bought 7 cases of apples each containing 40 lb. at 30s. per case and sold the apples at $10\frac{1}{2}d.$ per lb. Find (i) his total profit; (ii) his profit on 1 cwt.

42. A merchant bought a ton of oranges for £60 13s. 4d. If, in selling them, he made a profit of £14, what was the selling price per lb.?

43. How many bags of coal, each containing 1 cwt. 1 qr., can be filled from a truck which contains 9 tons 3 cwt. 2 qr. 11 lb. and how much will be left over?

44. A grocer buys 1 cwt. of tea for £28. What does it cost him per lb.? If he had bought the tea at 4d. per lb. less, how many more lb. could he have bought for the same money?

45. Part of a quantity of flour weighing 1 ton 1 cwt. 19 lb. is wrapped up in 7-lb. bags and the remainder in 4-lb. bags. There are one hundred and fifty-three 7-lb. bags. Find the number of 4-lb. bags.

46. A grocer buys tea at £29 8s. per cwt. and sells it so as to gain $7\frac{1}{2}d.$ per lb. What does he charge per packet of 7 lb.?

47. Ten wagons of coal, each containing 12 tons, were bought for £423. Four were sold at £48 per wagon and the remainder at 5s. 9d. per cwt. What was the total profit?

48. A grocer bought 3 cwt. 1 qr. 24 lb. of tea for £89 14s. 6d. He sold $1\frac{1}{2}$ cwt. at 5s. 6d. per lb. and the remainder at 5s. 9d. per lb. Find (i) his total profit; (ii) the cost price per lb. of tea.

49. A coal merchant buys 4 tons 5 cwt. of coal for £20 5s. He sells $2\frac{3}{4}$ tons at 5s. 6d. per cwt. and the rest at 5s. 9d. per cwt. Find his total profit.

50. A dealer bought 1 cwt. of coffee at 5s. 4d. per lb. and mixed it with $1\frac{1}{2}$ cwt. of coffee at 5s. per lb. If he wishes to make a profit of 6 guineas, at what price per lb. must he sell the mixture?

EXERCISE 1c

LENGTH

(a) Addition

1. yd.	ft.	in.	2. ch.	yd.	ft.	in.	3. fur.	yd.	ft.	in.
15	1	10	7	17	2	5	5	97	0	6
27	0	9	8	13	1	8	3	53	1	3
31	2	11	9	12	0	10	7	165	2	9
39	1	7	5	19	2	6	6	139	0	7

4.	ml.	fur.	ch.	yd.	ft.	in.
	15	7	9	17	2	5
	23	6	7	13	1	7
	31	5	6	12	0	11
	47	3	8	19	2	9

5.	ml.	fur.	yd.	ft.	in.
	34	6	183	1	6
	29	7	205	0	8
	41	4	167	2	10
	57	2	173	1	7

Find the sum of:

6. 15 yd. 5 in.;   2 ft. 9 in.;   13 yd. 1 ft.;   19 yd. 2 ft. 7 in.
7. 7 fur. 9 ch. 2 ft. 11 in.;   7 ch. 1 ft. 9 in.;
    5 fur. 17 yds. 8 in.;   6 fur. 5 ch. 19 yd.

Add together:

8. 5 ml. 6 fur. 17 yd. 2 ft. 5 in.;   8 ml. 19 ch. 15 yd. 1 ft. 7 in.;
    9 ml. 7 fur. 5 ch. 9 in.;   7 ml. 12 yd. 2 ft. 10 in.
9. 13 ml. 5 fur. 113 yd. 7 in.;   16 ml. 4 fur. 2 ft. 11 in;
    17 ml. 6 fur. 105 yd. 1 ft.;   19 ml. 7 fur. 203 yd. 2 ft. 9 in.

(b) **Subtraction**

10.	yd.	ft.	in.
	27	0	9
	19	1	11

11.	ch.	yd.	ft.	in.
	9	17	1	7
	6	19	2	9

12.	fur.	yd.	ft.	in.
	7	143	0	5
	4	167	2	6

13.	ml.	fur.	yd.	ft.	in.
	19	6	198	1	9
	16	7	205	1	10

14.	ml.	fur.	ch.	yd.	ft.	in.
	25	5	6	17	1	3
	21	7	9	20	2	7

15. From 5 ml. 7 ch. 1 ft. 3 in. subtract 3 ml. 4 fur. 19 yd. 7 in.
16. By how much is 12 ml. 3 fur. 132 yd. 5 in. greater than 9 ml. 7 fur. 211 yd. 2 ft. 7 in.?
17. Which is the greater and by how much:
        (i) 7 ml. 5 fur. 154 yd. 9 in.
    or (ii) 7 ml. 4 fur. 9 ch. 17 yd. 2 ft.?
18. Subtract the sum of 13 ml. 7 fur. 9 yd. 2 ft. 5 in. and 16 ml. 9 ch. 13 yd. 4 in. from 40 miles.

(c) Multiplication

19. ch.	yd.	ft.	in.		20. fur.	yd.	ft.	in.		21. fur.	ch.	yd.	ft.	in.
17	2	11			139	1	9			7	15	0	7	
		×35					×43						×57	

22. ml.	fur.	ch.	yd.	ft.	in.		23. ml.	fur.	yd.	ft.	in.
7	9	17	1	5			2	5	103	0	7
			×63							×75	

24. ml.	fur.	ch.	yd.	ft.	in.
3	6	9	13	2	8
				×87	

(d) Division

25. Divide 772 yd. 2 ft. 5 in. by 43
26. „   407 ch. 13 yd. 0 ft. 11 in. by 53
27. „   486 fur. 7 ch. 9 yd. 2 ft. 5 in. by 61
28. „   147 ml. 6 fur. 5 ch. 21 yd. 5 in. by 79

Using factors
29. Divide 81 ml. 4 fur. 6 yd. 2 ft. by 48
30. „   155 ml. 6 fur. 2 ch. 6 yd. 2 ft. 3 in. by 63

(e) Reduction

31. Reduce to inches: 17 yd. 2 ft. 9 in.
32. „   „ feet: 7 fur. 138 yd. 1 ft.
33. „   „ yards: 5 ml. 6 fur. 8 ch. 17 yd.
34. „   „ inches: 6 fur. 154 yd. 2 ft. 7 in.
35. „   „ inches: 3 ml. 5 fur. 7 ch. 17 yd. 1 ft. 9 in.
36. „   „ yd., ft., in.:   634 inches
37. „   „ fur., ch., yd., ft.:   1,743 feet
38. „   „ ml., fur., ch., yd.:   3,521 yards
39. „   „ fur., yd., ft., in.:   13,521 inches
40. „   „ ml., fur., ch., yd., ft., in.: 124,327 inches

(f) Miscellaneous

41. How many pieces of ribbon 2 ft. 3 in. long can be cut from a roll of ribbon $60\frac{1}{2}$ yd. long? What length of ribbon is left over?

42. A bicycle wheel measures 7 ft. 4 in. round the rim. How many times will it turn in travelling a distance of 2 miles?

43. A man in walking 100 yards takes 132 paces. How many paces would he take in walking round the world, supposing that distance to be 25,000 miles?

44. A globe is made so that a distance on the earth is 12 million times as great as on the globe. What is the distance, to the nearest mile, between two places, A and B, which are 3 inches apart on the globe?

45. The distance between two places is 126,720 times the distance as it appears on the map. How many inches on the map will represent an actual distance of 48 miles?

46. The length of a Guardsman's step is 29 in. and that of a farmer is 1 yd. If the Guardsman takes 756 steps in walking a certain distance, how many steps does the farmer take in walking the same distance? Express this distance in fur., ch., yd.

47. A bale of cloth contains 200 yd. The lengths required for a gent's three-piece suit, a gent's two-piece suit and a lady's costume are 6 yd., 5 yd. and 4 yd. respectively. Assuming the same number of each is made, find this number when 5 bales are used. What could be made with the remnant left over in each bale?

48. The rungs in a ladder are 1 ft. 1 in. apart. What is the length of a ladder having 20 rungs? How many rungs, 1 ft. 2 in. apart, would there be in another ladder of the same length?

49. The distance between successive telegraph poles is 70 yd. How many such poles are there in a distance of $17\frac{1}{2}$ miles beginning and ending with a pole? In this distance there are 385 poles for electric cables. How far are these apart? (To nearest yard.)

50. The lengths of the eighteen holes of a golf course are 172, 343, 456, 312, 152, 351, 476, 258, 355, 492, 361, 285, 316, 191, 393, 306, 151, 197 yd. respectively. Find the total length of the course in miles and yards. Which is the longer distance and by how much— the first 9 holes *or* the second 9 holes?

EXERCISE ID

TIME

(a) Addition

1. hr.	min.	sec.
19	29	23
17	23	34
21	37	55
14	43	37

2. dy.	hr.	min.
37	15	43
23	21	41
16	7	29
19	23	51

3. wk.	dy.	hr.	min.
2	3	21	37
4	6	15	21
7	5	17	43
3	4	23	39

4. yr.	wk.	dy.	hr.	min.
5	17	6	17	43
13	34	1	21	27
17	37	5	19	51
12	21	3	7	36

5. mth.	wk.	dy.	hr.	min.	sec.
7	3	5	19	37	25
11	0	2	23	19	31
13	1	0	15	41	52
9	2	6	12	38	43

Add together:

6. 17 hr. 25 min. 19 sec.; 9 hr. 17 min. 31 sec.;
21 hr. 49 sec.; 41 min. 30 sec.

7. 27 dy. 13 hr. 41 min.; 23 dy. 19 min.; 17 hr. 23 min.;
16 dy. 47 min.

8. 3 wk. 19 hr. 31 min.; 6 dy. 12 hr. 19 min.; 5 wk. 3 dy. 29 min.;
2 wk. 6 dy. 19 hr.

9. 43 wk. 3 dy. 13 hr. 31 min.; 11 yr. 4 dy. 23 hr. 39 min.;
15 yr. 41 wk. 17 hr. 43 min.; 9 yr. 5 dy. 29 min.

10. 9 mth. 6 dy. 29 min.; 3 wk. 17 hr. 41 sec.;
12 mth. 19 hr. 39 min. 47 sec.; 8 wk. 3 dy. 27 sec.

(b) Subtraction

11. hr.	min.	sec.
19	35	23
13	41	37

12. dy.	hr.	min.
17	19	41
14	23	53

13. wk.	dy.	hr.	min.
13	3	17	37
9	5	19	45

14. yr.	wk.	dy.	hr.	min.
13	43	3	13	31
10	49	5	17	48

15. mth.	wk.	dy.	hr.	min.	sec.
25	2	5	19	41	17
19	3	6	23	53	32

16. From 13 hr. 25 min. 37 sec. take 10 hr. 31 min. 49 sec.

17. Which is the longer time and by how much:
(i) 6 dy. 23 hr. 41 min. *or* (ii) 167 hr. 59 min. 33 sec.?

18. By how much is 5 wk. 6 dy. 19 hr. 57 min. longer than 4 wk. 5 dy. 21 hr. 41 min.?

19. Subtract 3 yr. 47 wk. 5 dy. 21 hr. 48 min. 51 sec. from 5 yr. 5 hr. 5 sec.

20. From the sum of 7 mth. 5 dy. 19 hr. 37 min. 53 sec. and 4 mth. 6 dy. 47 min. subtract 2 mth. 3 wk. 21 hr. 57 sec.

(c) Multiplication

21. hr.	min.	sec.	**22.** dy.	hr.	min.	**23.** wk.	dy.	hr.	min.
3	17	23	5	19	37	3	5	21	43
		×17			×23				×39

24. yr.	wk.	dy.	hr.	min.	**25.** mth.	wk.	dy.	hr.	min.	sec.
1	43	3	17	51	7	3	5	21	37	53
				×57						×79

(d) Division

26. Divide 138 hr. 59 min. 11 sec. by 37

27.   „   246 dy. 11 hr. 42 min. 47 sec. by 43

28.   „   190 wk. 2 dy. 20 hr. 37 min. 44 sec. by 67

Using factors:

29. Divide 94 yr. 32 wk. 4 dy. 20 hr. 40 min. by 56

30.   „   212 mth. 2 wk. 6 dy. 20 hr. 49 min. 12 sec. by 72

(e) Reduction

31. Reduce to seconds: 5 hr. 27 min. 43 sec.

32.   „   „ minutes: 6 dy. 17 hr. 47 min.

33.   „   „ seconds: 4 wk. 3 dy. 19 hr. 51 min.

34.   „   „ minutes:
2 yr. 47 wk. 5 dy. 21 hr. 39 min.

35.   „   „ seconds:
9 mth. 2 wk. 6 dy. 19 hr. 43 min. 51 sec.

36. Reduce to hr., min., sec.: 25,321 sec.

37.   „   „ dy., hr., min.: 10,478 min.

38.   „   „ wk., dy., hr., min.: 63,259 min.

39.   „   „ yr., wk., dy., hr., min.: 3,452,678 min.

40.   „   „ mth., wk., dy., hr., min., sec.: 7,563,241 sec.

(*f*) **Miscellaneous**

41. A bus runs at 24 miles per hour. How far does it go between 8.45 a.m. and 11.30 p.m.?

42. A daily newspaper (Sunday excluded) was numbered 45,231 on Saturday, 14th January 1956. What was the number on Wednesday, 18th July 1956?

43. Find the number of days between 15th November 1955 and 17th March 1956 (including one of these dates).

44. The moon makes a complete revolution (360 degrees) in its orbit in 28 dy. 12 hr. How long will it take to move in its orbit through (i) 90 degrees and (ii) 25 degrees?

45. The length of a year is exactly 365 dy. 5 hr. 48 min. 48 sec. What will be the error in the calendar at the end of 100 years in which there are 24 leap years?

46. A man runs round a race track 28 times in 1 hr. 1 min. 34 sec. Find how long (to the nearest second) he took to run each lap, assuming that all the laps were run in the same time.

47. An express train is travelling at a speed of 56 miles per hour. Find, in feet, the distance it will travel in 1 sec.

48. The new moon in January 1948 was on the 11th day at 7.44 a.m. and in February 1948 on the 10th day at 3.02 a.m. From this information find how long it takes the moon to make a complete revolution in its orbit.

49. On March 21st the sun rises at 6.01 a.m. and sets at 6.14 p.m. and on September 21st the sun rises at 5.44 a.m. and sets at 6.02 p.m. Which is the longer day and by how much?

50. The time between successive morning and afternoon high tides at London Bridge is 12 hr. 28 min. and the time between successive afternoon and morning high tides at London Bridge is 12 hr. 6 min. If the morning high tide on January 11th was at 1.41 a.m., find when the afternoon high tide took place on January 14th.

EXERCISE IE

CAPACITY

(a) Addition

1.	gall.	qt.	pt.
	5	3	1
	7	1	0
	6	0	1
	9	2	1

2.	gall.	qt.	pt.	gills
	9	1	0	3
	11	3	1	1
	13	0	1	2
	7	2	0	3

3.	qr.	bush.	pk.
	24	5	3
	17	7	1
	31	6	0
	29	3	2

4.	qr.	bush.	pk.	gall.
	57	5	2	1
	61	7	3	0
	19	6	1	1
	24	4	3	1

5.	qr.	bush.	pk.	gall.	pt.
	17	3	0	1	5
	34	6	1	0	7
	29	4	3	0	3
	43	2	2	1	6

Add together:

6. 9 gall. 1 pt. 3 gills; 7 gall. 3 qt. 1 gill;
2 qt. 1 pt. 2 gills; 5 gall. 1 pt.

7. 13 qr. 7 bush. 3 pk.; 7 qr. 2 pk.; 5 bush. 1 pk.;
11 qr. 4 bush.

8. 7 qr. 4 bush. 3 pk. 1 gall.; 12 qr. 5 bush. 2 pk.;
7 bush. 1 pk. 1 gall.; 9 qr. 1 gall.

9. 7 bush. 3 pk. 1 gall. 3 qt.; 9 bush. 1 gall. 2 qt.;
2 pk. 1 qt.; 5 bush. 2 pk. 2 qt.

10. 13 bush. 3 pk. 1 gall. 4 pt.; 5 bush. 2 pk. 1 gall. 6 pt.;
19 qr. 4 bush. 3 pk. 2 pt.; 27 qr. 4 bush. 3 pk. 1 gall.

(b) Subtraction

11.	gall.	qt.	pt.
	13	2	0
	9	3	1

12.	gall.	qt.	pt.	gills
	17	1	0	2
	12	3	1	3

13.	qr.	bush.	pk.
	23	6	1
	19	7	3

14.	qr.	bush.	pk.	gall.
	29	5	0	1
	23	7	2	1

15.	qr.	bush.	pk.	gall.	pt.
	31	4	2	0	5
	27	6	3	1	7

16. From 7 gall. 1 pt. 2 gills subtract 4 gall. 2 qt. 3 gills.

17. By how much does 24 qr. 6 bush. 1 pk. exceed 19 qr. 7 bush. 3 pk.?

18. Take 47 qr. 3 pk. 1 gall. from 51 qr. 2 bush.

19. Which is greater and by how much?
    (i) 7 qr. 2 bush. 1 pk. 2 qt. 1 pt.
  or (ii) 57 bush. 3 pk. 1 gall. 5 pt.

20. From the sum of 27 qr. 3 pk. 5 pt. and 7 bush. 1 gall. 4 pt. subtract the difference of 19 qr. 5 bush. 1 gall. and 13 qr. 1 pk. 7 pt.

(*c*) Multiplication

21.

gall.	qt.	pt.
7	2	1
		×37

22.

gall.	qt.	pt.	gills
9	3	0	3
			×49

23.

qr.	bush.	pk.
17	7	3
		×56

24.

qr.	bush.	pk.	gall.
25	7	3	1
			×63

25.

qr.	bush.	pk.	gall.	pt.
38	7	3	0	6
				×79

(*d*) Division

26. 106 gall. 1 qt. 1 pt. by 37
27. 154 gall. 2 qt. 0 pt. 1 gill by 43
28. 112 qr. 1 bush. 3 pk. by 57

Divide by factors:

29. 103 qr. 2 bush. 3 pk. 1 gall. by 35
30. 171 qr. 7 bush. 1 gall. 3 pt. by 63

(*e*) Reduction

31. Reduce to pints: 23 gall. 3 qt. 1 pt.
32.   „   „ gills: 17 gall. 2 qt. 1 pt. 3 gills
33.   „   „ pecks: 35 qr. 7 bush. 3 pk.
34.   „   „ gallons: 29 qr. 5 bush. 2 pk. 1 gall.
35.   „   „ pints: 15 qr. 6 bush. 1 pk. 7 pt.
36. Reduce to gall., qt., pt.:   127 pints
37.   „   „ gall., qt., pt., gills: 539 gills
38.   „   „ qr., bush., pk.:   476 pecks
39.   „   „ qr., bush., pk., gall.:   937 gallons
40.   „   „ qr., bush., pk., gall., pt.: 7,545 pints

(*f*) **Miscellaneous**

41. A merchant bought 48 gallons of oil at 7*s*. per gallon and sold it at 1*s*. 1*d*. per pint. What profit did he make?

42. In a canteen, a bottle containing $\frac{1}{3}$ of a pint of milk is sold for $1\frac{1}{2}d$. The milkman is paid £12 16*s*. $1\frac{1}{2}d$. for the week's supply. How much milk did he supply, in gall., qt., pt.?

43. The milk production on a certain farm is 120 gallons per day. If this milk is sold at 7*d*. a pint and the cost of production is 2*s*. $4\frac{3}{4}d$. per gallon, what is the weekly profit?

44. If 1 pint of water weighs $1\frac{1}{4}$ lb., what is the weight of milk in a 10-gallon can? (Milk is 1·04 times as heavy as water.)

45. A wine merchant buys 126 gallons of wine and bottles it into an equal number of quart, pint and two-gill bottles. How many bottles of each size has he? If he buys the wine for £484, at what price per pint bottle should he sell it to make a profit of £20?

46. At a sale 3,403 dozen bottles and 2,052 dozen half-bottles of wine are sold. Find the amount of wine in gallons, given that 6 bottles = 12 half-bottles = 1 gallon.

47. A person buys 325 gallons of spirit at £2 a gallon. How much water must he add to it so that he may gain £40 and retail the mixture at 3*s*. 9*d*. per pint?

48. A mixture is made up of 6 gallons of ale at 3*s*. 4*d*. per gallon, 3 gallons at 1*s*. 6*d*. per quart, 4 gallons at $11\frac{1}{4}d$. per pint and 12 gallons at 2*s*. 8*d*. per gallon. How much per pint is the mixture worth?

49. A man drinks $2\frac{1}{2}$ pints of beer per day (Sunday excluded). How much did he drink in 1955? If beer costs $7\frac{1}{2}d$. per pint, how much would the man save by drinking water instead?

50. A householder takes 3 pints of milk on odd and 2 pints on even days of the month. If his bill for July was £2 8*s*. 9*d*. what was the price of milk per pint during that month?

2

Short Methods

1. Multiplication by 25

Example. $37 \times 25 = 37 \times \dfrac{100}{4} = \dfrac{3700}{4} = 925$

RULE. To multiply any number by 25, add **two** zeroes to number (i.e. × 100) and divide by 4.

This method may be used for multiplication by numbers near 25.

Example. $73 \times 27 = 73 \times 25 + 73 \times 2 = 1825 + 146 = 1971$

2. Multiplication by 125

Example. $347 \times 125 = 347 \times \dfrac{1000}{8} = \dfrac{347000}{8} = 43,375$

RULE. To multiply any number by 125, add **three** zeroes to number (i.e. × 1000) and divide by 8.

This method may be used for multiplication by numbers near 125.

Example. $543 \times 123 = 543 \times 125 - 543 \times 2 = 67,875 - 1,086 = 66,789$

EXERCISE 2A

Multiply the following numbers by 25.

1. 17	**2.** 29	**3.** 35	**4.** 143
5. 259	**6.** 387	**7.** 731	**8.** 973

Multiply the following numbers by 125.

9. 78	**10.** 93	**11.** 127	**12.** 261
	13. 459	**14.** 531	**15.** 746

Evaluate:

16. 27×26	**17.** 89×128	**18.** 39×28
19. 104×127	**20.** 45×29	**21.** 138×126
22. 53×23	**23.** 273×124	**24.** 69×22
	25. 547×123	

Costing

1. *Cost of 12 articles*

   Example. Find the cost of 12 articles at 1*s*. 5*d*. each

   Cost of 12 articles at 1*s*. 5*d*. each $= 17 \times 12$ pence

   $$= \frac{17 \times 12}{12} \text{ shillings}$$

   $$= 17s.$$

Note that the number of **pence** in the cost of 1 article
   $=$ the number of **shillings** in the cost of 12 articles.

RULE. To find the cost of 12 articles given the cost of 1 article, reduce the cost of 1 article to pence and call the pence shillings.

This method may be applied to finding the cost of around 12 articles.

Example. Cost of 14 articles at 2*s*. 2*d*. each

$$= 26s. + 4s. \ 4d.$$
$$= 30s. \ 4d.$$
$$= £1 \ 10s. \ 4d.$$

Example. Cost of 11 articles at 1*s*. $5\frac{1}{2}d$.

$$= 17s. \ 6d. - 1s. \ 5\frac{1}{2}d.$$
$$= 16s. \ 0\frac{1}{2}d.$$

2. *Cost of 20 articles*

   Example. Find the cost of 20 articles at 2*s*. 3*d*. each

   Cost of 20 articles at 2*s*. 3*d*. each $= 2\frac{1}{4} \times 20s.$

   $$= £\frac{2\frac{1}{4} \times 20}{20}$$

   $$= £2 \ 5s.$$

Note that the number of **shillings** in the cost of 1 article
   $=$ the number of **pounds** in the cost of 20 articles.

RULE. To find the cost of 20 articles given the cost of 1 article, reduce the cost of 1 article to shillings and call the shillings pounds.

This method may be applied to finding the cost of around 20 articles.

Example. Cost of 23 articles at 3s. 4d. each

$$= £3\ 6s.\ 8d. + 10s.$$
$$= £3\ 16s.\ 8d.$$

Example. Cost of 18 articles at 2s. $7\frac{1}{2}d$. each

$$= £2\ 12s.\ 6d. - 5s.\ 3d.$$
$$= £2\ 7s.\ 3d.$$

It is clear that this result can be applied conveniently in the table of weight.

Example. What is the total weight of 20 sacks each containing $1\frac{1}{4}$ cwt.?

$$\text{Weight of 1 sack} = 1\frac{1}{4}\ \text{cwt.}$$
$$\therefore \text{Weight of 20 sacks} = 1\frac{1}{4}\ \text{tons}$$

Using similar rules, it is possible for us to cost '240', '480', '960' articles since 240 pence = £1; 480 halfpennies = £1; 960 farthings = £1.

3. *Example.* Cost of 240 articles at 1s. $2\frac{1}{2}d$. each = £14 10s.

RULE. Reduce the cost of 1 article to pence and call the pence pounds.

Example. Cost of 243 articles at 3s. $3\frac{1}{2}d$. each

$$= £39\ 10s. + 9s.\ 10\frac{1}{2}d.$$
$$= £39\ 19s.\ 10\frac{1}{2}d.$$

4. *Example.* Cost of 480 articles at 2s. $1\frac{1}{2}d$. each = £51

RULE. Reduce cost of 1 article to halfpence and call the halfpence pounds.

Example. Cost of 478 articles at 1s. $10\frac{1}{2}d$. each

$$= £45 - 3s.\ 9d.$$
$$= £44\ 16s.\ 3d.$$

5. *Example.* Cost of 960 articles at 1s. $5\frac{3}{4}d$. each = £71

RULE. Reduce the cost of 1 article to farthings and call the farthings pounds.

Example. Cost of 957 articles at 2s. $2\frac{1}{4}d$. each

$$= £105 - 6s.\ 6\frac{3}{4}d.$$
$$= £104\ 13s.\ 5\frac{1}{4}d.$$

EXERCISE 2B

With as little working as possible, find the cost of the following articles:

1. 12 at 1s. 7d. each
2. 12 at 2s. 3½d. each
3. 12 at 3s. 7¼d. each
4. 14 at 1s. 9d. each
5. 15 at 2s. 4¾d. each
6. 11 at 3s. 2½d. each
7. 9 at 4s. 1½d. each
8. 24 at 3s. 2d. each
9. 36 at 5s. 4d. each
10. 48 at 2s. 7½d. each
11. 240 at 2s. 5d. each
12. 240 at 3s. 4½d. each
13. 240 at 4s. 2¾d. each
14. 241 at 2s. 8d. each
15. 243 at 3s. 5½d. each
16. 238 at 4s. 3¼d. each
17. 236 at 5s. 2¾d. each
18. 480 at 2s. 4½d. each
19. 480 at 3s. 5d. each
20. 480 at 5s. 3¼d. each
21. 482 at 2s. 9d. each
22. 484 at 3s. 2½d. each
23. 479 at 4s. 1¾d. each
24. 477 at 6s. 2¼d. each
25. 960 at 1s. 7d. each
26. 960 at 2s. 3½d. each
27. 960 at 3s. 2¾d. each
28. 961 at 3s. 8d. each
29. 963 at 4s. 5½d. each
30. 958 at 5s. 1¼d. each

EXERCISE 2C

Find the total cost for the following bills:

1. 12 lb. bacon at 3s. 6d. per lb.
   11 lb. cheese at 2s. 8d. per lb.
   13 pots jam at 2s. 10d. per pot
   24 lb. sugar at 7½d. per lb.

2. 14 lb. tea at 7s. 2d. per lb.
   11 lb. coffee at 8s. 4d. per lb.
   12 lb. gammon at 7s. 4d. per lb.
   25 jars honey at 5s. 2d. per jar

3. 13 lb. granulated sugar at 7½d. per lb.
   23 lb. cube sugar at 9½d. per lb.
   36 lb. caster sugar at 9d. per lb.
   11 lb. icing sugar at 1s. 2½d. per lb.

4. 241 packets of Daz at 11*d*. per pkt.
480 packets of Fab at 10½*d*. per pkt.
478 packets of Oxydol at 5*d*. per pkt.
960 packets of Persil at 5½*d*. per pkt.

5. 14 lb. cookeen at 1*s*. 10*d*. per lb.
10 lb. margarine at 1*s*. 7½*d*. per lb.
11 jars marmalade at 2*s*. 8½*d*. per jar
13 lb. cheese at 2*s*. 10*d*. per lb.

3

Factors, H.C.F., L.C.M.

PRIME AND COMPOSITE NUMBERS

Whole numbers can be conveniently divided into two classes:

(A) **Prime Numbers** and (B) **Composite Numbers**

(A) A **prime** number is one which cannot be divided exactly by any other number (except itself and unity), e.g. 3, 5, 7, 11 etc. are prime numbers.

(B) A **composite** number is one which can be divided exactly by some other number, *or* a **composite** number is one which is not **prime,** e.g. 4, 6, 8, 9 etc. are composite numbers.

Tests of Divisibility

The following tests of divisibility will be found useful in determining whether a number is prime or composite:

1. A number is divisible by 2 when its units digit is an even number, e.g. 152.

2. A number is divisible by 3 when the sum of its digits is divisible by 3, e.g. 5,796.

3. A number is divisible by 4 when the number formed by its last two digits is divisible by 4, e.g. 5,784 is divisible by 4 because 84 is divisible by 4.

4. A number is divisible by 5 when its units digit is 0 or 5, e.g. 60 or 75.

5. A number is divisible by 8 when the number formed by its last three digits is divisible by 8, e.g. 13,656 is divisible by 8 because 656 is divisible by 8.

6. A number is divisible by 9 when the sum of its digits is divisible by 9, e.g. 537,624 is divisible by 9 because $5+3+7+6+2+4=27$ is divisible by 9.

7. A number is divisible by 10 when its units digit is 0.

34

EXERCISE 3A

State whether the following numbers are divisible by 2, 3, 4, 5, 8, 9 or 10.

1. 168	**2.** 255	**3.** 381	**4.** 536
5. 759	**6.** 1,510	**7.** 6,252	**8.** 7,648
9. 9,825	**10.** 13,842	**11.** 21,072	**12.** 34,515

         13. 67,352   **14.** 84,560   **15.** 92,175

EXERCISE 3B

State which of the following numbers are **prime** and which are **composite**.

1. 54	**2.** 63	**3.** 79	**4.** 93
5. 117	**6.** 131	**7.** 165	**8.** 203
9. 253	**10.** 317	**11.** 369	**12.** 411
13. 473	**14.** 567	**15.** 623	**16.** 689
17. 721	**18.** 807	**19.** 879	**20.** 927

Write down all the prime numbers between

         21. 50 and 70   **22.** 90 and 120
         23. 170 and 200   **24.** 210 and 250
            25. 360 and 400

FACTORS

Any number which divides exactly into another number is called a **factor** of that number, e.g. 9 is a factor of 63.

Where the factor is a prime number, it is referred to as a **prime factor**, e.g. 12 can be divided exactly by the prime factors 2 and 3.

Hence, from its definition every composite number will have prime factors.

It is frequently useful to express such a number in terms of its prime factors.

Example 1. Express 2,520 in prime factors.

```
2 | 2520
2 | 1260
2 |  630
3 |  315
3 |  105
5 |   35
7 |    7
  |    1
```

$$\therefore \ 2,520 = 2 \times 2 \times 2 \times 3 \times 3 \times 5 \times 7$$
$$= 2^3 . 3^2 . 5 . 7$$

Note. Where a factor is repeated, this repetition is shown by an index.

Thus $2 \times 2 \times 2 = 2^3$

It is clear from this example that the method of finding the prime factors of any number is that of repeated division beginning with the lowest prime number which is a factor.

EXERCISE 3C

Find the prime factors of each of the following number:

1. 18	**2.** 24	**3.** 32	**4.** 72
5. 108	**6.** 144	**7.** 196	**8.** 234
9. 396	**10.** 468	**11.** 484	**12.** 560
13. 588	**14.** 702	**15.** 990	**16.** 1,008
17. 1,144	**18.** 3,465	**19.** 7,560	**20.** 9,125
21. 9,153	**22.** 10,296	**23.** 13,500	**24.** 46,662
	25. 59,829		

HIGHEST COMMON FACTOR

When two or more numbers can each be divided exactly by a certain number, then that number is called a **common factor** of the given numbers.

Thus, since the numbers 8, 12, 20 can each be divided exactly by 4, then 4 is a common factor of these numbers.

The highest number which divides exactly two or more numbers is referred to as the **highest common factor** of these numbers. For convenience, the letters H.C.F. are used for Highest Common Factor.

The simplest method of finding the H.C.F. of a group of numbers is that of finding the prime factors of each number in turn by the method illustrated in the last set of examples.

Example 2.—Find the H.C.F. of 36, 42 and 48.

$$36 = 2 \times 2 \times 3 \times 3 \qquad = 2^2 . 3^2$$
$$42 = 2 \times 3 \times 7 \qquad = 2.3.7$$
$$48 = 2 \times 2 \times 2 \times 2 \times 3 = 2^4 . 3$$

Each of these numbers has 2 and 3 as common factors.

$$\therefore \text{ H.C.F.} = 2.3 = 6$$

Example 3. Find the H.C.F. of 48, 84, and 132.

$$48 = 2 \times 2 \times 2 \times 2 \times 3 = 2^4 . 3$$
$$84 = 2 \times 2 \times 3 \times 7 \qquad = 2^2 . 3 . 7$$
$$132 = 2 \times 2 \times 3 \times 11 \qquad = 2^2 . 3 . 11$$
$$\therefore \text{ H.C.F.} = 2^2 . 3 = 12$$

EXERCISE 3D. *Oral*

State the H.C.F. in the following examples:

1. 4, 6	**2.** 9, 12	**3.** 12, 20
4. 15, 25	**5.** 18, 30	**6.** 20, 35
7. 24, 32	**8.** 27, 63	**9.** 32, 56
10. 8, 12, 24	**11.** 6, 15, 21	**12.** 10, 25, 30
13. 12, 18, 42	**14.** 16, 24, 32	**15.** 24, 36, 60

EXERCISE 3E

Using the method of prime factors, find the H.C.F. in the following examples:

1. 27, 36	**2.** 40, 56
3. 48, 72	**4.** 54, 81
5. 56, 98	**6.** 72, 150
7. 112, 144	**8.** 240, 264
9. 462, 546	**10.** 484, 858

11. 468, 540	**12.** 639, 873
13. 781, 1,441	**14.** 808, 1,112
15. 1,260, 1,575	**16.** 1,512, 1,584
17. 2,520, 3,234	**18.** 434, 1,582, 2,114
19. 935, 1,190, 1,309	**20.** 1,001, 1,573, 1,859

LOWEST COMMON MULTIPLE

If one number can be divided exactly by another number, then the first number is a **multiple** of the second. Thus 12 is a multiple of 3.

A number which can be divided exactly by each of a group of numbers is a **common multiple** of these numbers. Thus 36 is a common multiple of the numbers 3, 4 and 6.

The smallest number which can be divided exactly by each of a group of numbers is called the **lowest common multiple** of these numbers.

For convenience, the letters L.C.M. are used for Lowest Common Multiple.

Thus 12 is the L.C.M. of the numbers 3, 4 and 6.

Again, it is found that the simplest method of finding the L.C.M. of a group of numbers is by expressing each of the numbers in turn in terms of its prime factors.

Example 4. Find the L.C.M. of 12, 18 and 42.

EITHER,

$$12 = 2 \times 2 \times 3 = 2^2 . 3$$
$$18 = 2 \times 3 \times 3 = 2 . 3^2$$
$$42 = 2 \times 3 \times 7 = 2 . 3 . 7$$
$$\therefore \text{L.C.M.} = 2^2 . 3^2 . 7 = 252$$

OR,

2	12,	18,	42
2	6,	9,	21
3	3,	9,	21
3	1,	3,	7
7	1,	1,	7
	1,	1,	1

$$\therefore \text{L.C.M.} = 2^2 . 3^2 . 7 = 252$$

This alternative method is really that of reducing all of the numbers to prime factors at the same time.

Example 5. Find the L.C.M. of 3, 6, 9, 12, 15, 18, 20, 21

2	3,	6,	9,	12,	15,	18,	20,	21
2				6,	15,	9,	10,	21
3				3,	15,	9,	5,	21
3				1,	5,	3,	5,	7
5				1,	5,	1,	5,	7
7				1,	1,	1,	1,	7
				1,	1,	1,	1,	1

$$\therefore \text{L.C.M.} = 2^2 . 3^2 . 5 . 7$$
$$= 1,260$$

Note. In the above example there is no need to investigate the multiples of 3, 6, 9 since any number which is a multiple of 18 will also be a multiple of these three numbers. Thus, so long as 18 is retained the numbers 3, 6, 9 may be disregarded.

EXERCISE 3F. *Oral*

State the L.C.M. of the following groups of numbers.

1. 4, 6
2. 8, 12
3. 9, 12
4. 2, 3, 4
5. 4, 6, 9
6. 6, 8, 12
7. 5, 8, 10
8. 3, 6, 8
9. 3, 8, 12
10. 5, 6, 12
11. 2, 4, 6, 8
12. 2, 3, 4, 5
13. 3, 6, 8, 12
14. 4, 5, 6, 10
15. 5, 8, 9, 12

EXERCISE 3G

Find the L.C.M. of the following groups of numbers.

1. 12, 16, 20
2. 18, 24, 27
3. 20, 25, 30
4. 24, 32, 36
5. 32, 40, 48
6. 16, 32, 64, 96
7. 18, 21, 35, 42
8. 18, 36, 54, 72
9. 42, 56, 70, 84
10. 54, 60, 66, 72
11. 2, 6, 10, 14, 18
12. 3, 6, 9, 12, 15
13. 6, 12, 24, 32, 40
14. 12, 16, 18, 27, 30
15. 4, 8, 12, 16, 20, 24
16. 5, 10, 15, 20, 25, 30
17. 8, 16, 18, 24, 32, 36
18. 15, 18, 20, 28, 45, 54

19. Even numbers between 10 and 20 inclusive.

20. Odd numbers between 21 and 27 inclusive.

21. Find the least number which can be divided by 9, 12, 16 and 18 and leave a remainder of 5 in each case.

22. Find, by prime factors, the H.C.F. and L.C.M. of 42, 63 and 147.

23. Find, by prime factors, the H.C.F. and L.C.M. of 78, 182, 156 and 286.

24. Find the least sum of money which can pay bills of either 1s. 6d., 1s. 9d. and 2s. 11d. each an exact number of times.

25. Find the least sum of money which will buy an exact number of yards of material at 6s. 3d. per yard, 8s. 4d. per yard and 8s. 9d. per yard.

26. What is the smallest sum of money from which an exact whole number of payments of 6s. 9d. or 13s. 4d. or £1 17s. 6d. or £2 16s. 3d. can be made ?

27. A man, A, can walk 40 miles a day, B 36 miles, C 32 miles and D 30 miles. Find the shortest journey which would occupy each one of them a complete number of days.

28. Three soldiers are walking together in step. The lengths of their strides are 28 in., 32 in. and 36 in. respectively. How far must they walk together before they are again in step?

29. Three church bells chime at intervals of 18, 24 and 32 seconds respectively. If they all begin at 10.45 a.m., when will they chime together again?

30. Three lights flash at intervals of 16, 18 and 25 seconds respectively. If they all flash together at 3.20 p.m., at what time will they next flash together?

4

Vulgar Fractions

Consider the accompanying diagram *which represents a block of chocolate divided into eight equal parts. Suppose this chocolate block is shared by three people* A, B *and* C as indicated.

A	B	C	C
B	B	C	C

Then, A receives 1 of the 8 equal parts (or **eighths**)

      B ,,   3 ,, 8 ,,   ,,

      C ,,   4 ,, 8 ,,   ,,

This can be abbreviated by saying that

    A receives **one**-eighth (written $\frac{1}{8}$)

    B ,,   **three**-eighths ($\frac{3}{8}$)

    C ,,   **four**-eighths ($\frac{4}{8}$)

These parts of the whole block of chocolate, namely $\frac{1}{8}$, $\frac{3}{8}$ and $\frac{4}{8}$, are referred to as **fractions** of the single block.

Hence, a **fraction** of a unit indicates one or more equal parts of the unit.

We are already familiar with $\frac{3}{4}d.$ as representing three-fourths of a penny, but let us consider this fraction $\frac{3}{4}$ more closely.

The fraction $\frac{3}{4}$ consists of two parts:

(*a*) 4 expresses the number of equal parts into which the unit is divided, that is, the denomination of the equal parts. Hence, it is called the **denominator.**

(*b*) 3 enumerates the number of these equal parts taken to form the fraction. Hence, it is called the **numerator.**

Fractions of this kind are called **vulgar fractions** (common fractions).

EXERCISE 4A. *Oral*

Express as vulgar fractions:

1. one-third
2. two-fifths
3. four-sevenths
4. twelve-nineteenths
5. seventeen-twenty-thirds
6. two-forty-sevenths
7. ten-sixty-thirds
8. nineteen-seventy-fourths
9. twenty-five-eighty-firsts
10. forty-three-ninety-ninths
11. seven-hundredths
12. eleven-three-hundredths
13. twenty-three-four-thousandths
14. one-hundred-and-three-five-thousandths
15. seven-thousand-and-seven-millionths

Express in words:

16. $\frac{1}{5}$　　17. $\frac{2}{3}$　　18. $\frac{5}{6}$　　19. $\frac{11}{19}$　　20. $\frac{19}{21}$

21. $\frac{3}{43}$　　22. $\frac{10}{61}$　　23. $\frac{16}{75}$　　24. $\frac{27}{83}$　　25. $\frac{41}{97}$

26. $\frac{11}{100}$　　27. $\frac{13}{500}$　　28. $\frac{271}{3000}$　　29. $\frac{1361}{4000}$　　30. $\frac{3517}{1000000}$

EXERCISE 4B. *Oral*

State the value of the following:

1. $\frac{1}{4}s.$　　2. $\frac{2}{3}s.$　　3. £$\frac{3}{4}$　　4. £$\frac{4}{5}$

5. £$\frac{1}{3}$　　6. $\frac{5}{12}$ of 1s.　　7. $\frac{3}{8}$ of 1s.　　8. $\frac{7}{20}$ of £1

9. $\frac{5}{8}$ of £1　　10. $\frac{5}{6}$ of £1　　11. $\frac{7}{16}$ lb.　　12. $\frac{3}{7}$ st.

13. $\frac{9}{14}$ qr.　　14. $\frac{5}{8}$ cwt.　　15. $\frac{3}{5}$ ton　　16. $\frac{1}{4}$ of 3 lb.

17. $\frac{5}{14}$ of 2 qr.　　18. $\frac{7}{8}$ of 4 st.　　19. $\frac{2}{7}$ of 2 cwt.　　20. $\frac{7}{10}$ of 3 tons

21. $\frac{2}{3}$ ft.　　22. $\frac{2}{9}$ yd.　　23. $\frac{5}{11}$ ch.　　24. $\frac{4}{5}$ fur.

25. $\frac{3}{4}$ ml.　　26. $\frac{13}{24}$ of 4 ft.　　27. $\frac{2}{3}$ of 2 yd.　　28. $\frac{11}{25}$ of 5 ch.

29. $\frac{18}{55}$ of 3 fur.　　30. $\frac{7}{220}$ of 11 ml.

The diagrams given on the opposite page represent three identical blocks of chocolate divided in different ways.

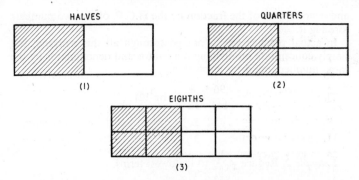

HALVES

QUARTERS

(1)

(2)

EIGHTHS

(3)

In diagram:

(1), the block of chocolate is divided into two-halves
(2), ,, ,, ,, ,, ,, ,, ,, four-quarters
(3), ,, ,, ,, ,, ,, ,, ,, eight-eighths

By comparing these different parts it will be clear that

one-half block of chocolate = two-quarter blocks of chocolate
= four-eighths of a block of chocolate

i.e. $\frac{1}{2}$ block of chocolate $= \frac{2}{4}$ blocks of chocolate
$= \frac{4}{8}$ of a block of chocolate

This illustrates the important principle of the equivalence of fractions, namely, that the value of a vulgar fraction remains unaltered when its numerator **and** denominator are multiplied or divided by the **same** number.

Thus $\frac{1}{3} = \frac{2}{6} = \frac{3}{9} = \frac{4}{12} =$ etc.

And this leads now to the process of reducing a vulgar fraction to its lowest terms.

Example 1. Reduce $\frac{96}{144}$ to its lowest terms.

Expressing the numerator and denominator in prime factors, we have

$$96 = 2 \times 2 \times 2 \times 2 \times 2 \times 2 \times 3$$
$$144 = 2 \times 2 \times 2 \times 2 \times 3 \times 3$$

$$\therefore \frac{96}{144} = \frac{2 \times 2 \times 2 \times 2 \times 2 \times 3}{2 \times 2 \times 2 \times 2 \times 3 \times 3} = \frac{2}{3}$$

Note that the result, $\frac{2}{3}$, is obtained by dividing the numerator

and denominator of the fraction by the H.C.F. of the two numbers forming it.

In actual practice we do not go through all this working, but simply concentrate on dividing numerator and denominator by the same number found by inspection.

Thus
$$\frac{96}{144} = \frac{8}{12} \ (\div \text{ by } 12)$$

$$= \frac{2}{3} \ (\div \text{ by } 4)$$

Example 2. Reduce $\frac{852}{1164}$ to its lowest terms.

$$\frac{852}{1164} = \frac{213}{291} \ (\div \text{ by } 4)$$

$$= \frac{71}{97} \ (\div \text{ by } 3)$$

EXERCISE 4C. *Oral*

Express the following vulgar fractions in their lowest terms:

1. $\frac{6}{8}$	**2.** $\frac{8}{10}$	**3.** $\frac{9}{15}$	**4.** $\frac{12}{16}$	**5.** $\frac{16}{20}$
6. $\frac{14}{21}$	**7.** $\frac{21}{35}$	**8.** $\frac{63}{70}$	**9.** $\frac{96}{160}$	**10.** $\frac{56}{64}$
11. $\frac{33}{121}$	**12.** $\frac{36}{48}$	**13.** $\frac{75}{125}$	**14.** $\frac{121}{440}$	**15.** $\frac{125}{275}$
16. $\frac{162}{198}$	**17.** $\frac{375}{625}$	**18.** $\frac{216}{396}$	**19.** $\frac{105}{150}$	**20.** $\frac{350}{525}$

EXERCISE 4D

Reduce the following vulgar fractions to their lowest terms:

1. $\frac{48}{112}$	**2.** $\frac{72}{168}$	**3.** $\frac{204}{228}$	**4.** $\frac{288}{384}$	**5.** $\frac{297}{396}$
6. $\frac{297}{462}$	**7.** $\frac{336}{448}$	**8.** $\frac{605}{660}$	**9.** $\frac{625}{925}$	**10.** $\frac{666}{810}$
11. $\frac{375}{1275}$	**12.** $\frac{968}{1056}$	**13.** $\frac{875}{1295}$	**14.** $\frac{756}{1386}$	**15.** $\frac{765}{1665}$
16. $\frac{591}{2167}$	**17.** $\frac{972}{3276}$	**18.** $\frac{1164}{1212}$	**19.** $\frac{1127}{1421}$	**20.** $\frac{1050}{2175}$
21. $\frac{1452}{2464}$	**22.** $\frac{1562}{2662}$	**23.** $\frac{1750}{2250}$	**24.** $\frac{5280}{5940}$	**25.** $\frac{6416}{9624}$

Frequently it is necessary to compare vulgar fractions or arrange them in order of magnitude. This is only possible when all the fractions are of the same denomination. Hence we express each fraction with the same denominator.

Example 3. Express $\frac{2}{3}$ and $\frac{3}{4}$ as fractions having the same denominator.

In the first instance the problem here is that of finding the smallest number into which each of the numbers 3 and 4 will divide without remainder, i.e. find the L.C.M. of 3 and 4.

$$\text{L.C.M. of 3 and 4} = 12$$

$$\therefore \frac{2}{3} = \frac{2 \times 4}{3 \times 4} = \frac{8}{12}$$

$$\text{and } \frac{3}{4} = \frac{3 \times 3}{4 \times 3} = \frac{9}{12}$$

Example 4. Which is the greater fraction, $\frac{8}{9}$ or $\frac{11}{12}$?

$$\text{L.C.M. of 9 and 12} = 36$$

$$\therefore \frac{8}{9} = \frac{32}{36}$$

$$\text{and } \frac{11}{12} = \frac{33}{36}$$

$$\therefore \frac{11}{12} \text{ is greater than } \frac{8}{9}$$

Example 5. Arrange in descending order of magnitude $\frac{5}{6}, \frac{7}{8}, \frac{11}{12}, \frac{13}{18}$.

$$\text{L.C.M. of 6, 8, 12 and 18} = 72$$

$$\frac{5}{6} = \frac{60}{72} \qquad \frac{7}{8} = \frac{63}{72}$$

$$\frac{11}{12} = \frac{66}{72} \qquad \frac{13}{18} = \frac{52}{72}$$

$$\therefore \text{ required descending order is } \frac{11}{12}, \frac{7}{8}, \frac{5}{6}, \frac{13}{18}$$

EXERCISE 4E. *Oral*

Express as fractions having the same denominator:

1. $\frac{1}{3}$ and $\frac{1}{2}$
2. $\frac{3}{4}$ and $\frac{1}{6}$
3. $\frac{5}{6}$ and $\frac{3}{8}$
4. $\frac{2}{5}$ and $\frac{3}{4}$
5. $\frac{2}{3}$ and $\frac{4}{5}$
6. $\frac{7}{8}$ and $\frac{5}{12}$
7. $\frac{1}{4}$ and $\frac{7}{16}$
8. $\frac{7}{12}$ and $\frac{13}{18}$
9. $\frac{1}{2}, \frac{2}{3}$ and $\frac{3}{5}$
10. $\frac{1}{4}, \frac{5}{6}$ and $\frac{7}{12}$
11. $\frac{1}{3}, \frac{2}{5}$ and $\frac{7}{10}$
12. $\frac{5}{8}, \frac{11}{16}$ and $\frac{13}{24}$

Which is the greater fraction?

13. $\frac{1}{2}$ or $\frac{1}{3}$
14. $\frac{1}{4}$ or $\frac{1}{5}$
15. $\frac{5}{6}$ or $\frac{3}{4}$
16. $\frac{4}{5}$ or $\frac{2}{3}$
17. $\frac{5}{8}$ or $\frac{7}{12}$
18. $\frac{3}{4}$ or $\frac{13}{16}$
19. $\frac{11}{12}$ or $\frac{13}{18}$
20. $\frac{11}{16}$ or $\frac{13}{24}$

EXERCISE 4F

Express as fractions having the same denominator:

1. $\frac{1}{2}, \frac{2}{3}, \frac{3}{4}$ **2.** $\frac{3}{4}, \frac{5}{6}, \frac{4}{9}$ **3.** $\frac{1}{6}, \frac{5}{8}, \frac{7}{12}$

4. $\frac{1}{2}, \frac{3}{4}, \frac{5}{6}, \frac{3}{8}$ **5.** $\frac{1}{4}, \frac{3}{5}, \frac{5}{6}, \frac{7}{10}$ **6.** $\frac{7}{12}, \frac{11}{16}, \frac{13}{20}$

7. $\frac{17}{20}, \frac{19}{25}, \frac{21}{30}$ **8.** $\frac{13}{24}, \frac{15}{32}, \frac{17}{36}$ **9.** $\frac{3}{4}, \frac{5}{8}, \frac{9}{16}, \frac{13}{24}$

10. $\frac{5}{6}, \frac{6}{7}, \frac{7}{12}, \frac{11}{14}$

Arrange the following fractions in descending order of magnitude:

11. $\frac{4}{5}, \frac{5}{8}, \frac{7}{10}$ **12.** $\frac{5}{6}, \frac{7}{8}, \frac{11}{12}$ **13.** $\frac{3}{5}, \frac{5}{6}, \frac{7}{12}$

14. $\frac{3}{4}, \frac{5}{7}, \frac{9}{14}$ **15.** $\frac{7}{8}, \frac{9}{10}, \frac{13}{16}$

Arrange the following fractions in ascending order of magnitude:

16. $\frac{2}{3}, \frac{3}{4}, \frac{3}{5}$ **17.** $\frac{4}{5}, \frac{5}{6}, \frac{7}{8}$ **18.** $\frac{5}{6}, \frac{5}{8}, \frac{7}{9}$

19. $\frac{7}{8}, \frac{11}{12}, \frac{13}{16}$ **20.** $\frac{5}{9}, \frac{7}{12}, \frac{11}{15}$

Arrange the following in descending order of magnitude:

	(1)	(2)	(3)
21.	$\frac{1}{2}$ of 3s. 6d;	$\frac{1}{3}$ of 4s. 6d.;	$\frac{1}{5}$ of 11s. 3d.
22.	$\frac{2}{3}$ of 5s.;	$\frac{3}{4}$ of 4s. 8d.;	$\frac{2}{5}$ of 6s. 8d.
23.	$\frac{5}{6}$ of £1;	$\frac{7}{8}$ of 24s.;	$\frac{8}{9}$ of 19s. 6d.
24.	$\frac{5}{7}$ of 1 st.;	$\frac{7}{8}$ of 12 lb.;	$\frac{11}{14}$ of 1 qr.
25.	$\frac{3}{4}$ of 1 ton;	$\frac{2}{3}$ of 21 cwt.;	$\frac{3}{5}$ of 2 tons
26.	$\frac{5}{12}$ of 1 yd.;	$\frac{8}{9}$ of 2 ft.;	$\frac{7}{10}$ of 25 in.
27.	$\frac{5}{8}$ of 1 ml.;	$\frac{3}{4}$ of 6 fur.;	$\frac{7}{10}$ of 1,320 yd.
28.	$\frac{5}{8}$ of 1 gal.;	$\frac{3}{4}$ of 6 qt.;	$\frac{4}{5}$ of 10 pt.
29.	$\frac{7}{12}$ of 1 hr.;	$\frac{9}{10}$ of 40 min.;	$\frac{5}{8}$ of 2 hr.
30.	$\frac{7}{12}$ of 1 day;	$\frac{2}{3}$ of $\frac{3}{4}$ day;	$\frac{3}{4}$ of 18 hr.

Vulgar Fractions may be divided into two groups, namely, **proper** and **improper** fractions.

A **proper** fraction is one in which the numerator is less than the denominator, e.g. $\frac{2}{3}$.

An **improper** fraction is one in which the numerator is greater than the denominator, e.g. $\frac{7}{4}$.

Now the improper fraction $\frac{7}{4}$ means seven-fourths of a unit

$$= \text{four-fourths} + \text{three-fourths}$$
$$= 1\frac{3}{4}$$

A quantity of this form, $1\frac{3}{4}$, consisting of a whole number (1) and a proper fraction ($\frac{3}{4}$), is called a **mixed number.**

EXERCISE 4G. *Oral*

Express as mixed numbers:

1. $\frac{8}{3}$ **2.** $\frac{21}{4}$ **3.** $\frac{7}{5}$ **4.** $\frac{71}{6}$ **5.** $\frac{12}{7}$

6. $\frac{117}{8}$ **7.** $\frac{37}{9}$ **8.** $\frac{93}{10}$ **9.** $\frac{48}{11}$ **10.** $\frac{53}{12}$

Express as improper fractions:

11. $1\frac{1}{3}$ **12.** $1\frac{3}{4}$ **13.** $2\frac{1}{5}$ **14.** $3\frac{5}{6}$ **15.** $7\frac{5}{7}$

16. $9\frac{3}{8}$ **17.** $11\frac{5}{9}$ **18.** $13\frac{3}{10}$ **19.** $17\frac{2}{11}$ **20.** $31\frac{5}{12}$

Find the value of:

21. $1\frac{3}{4}$ of £1   **22.** $2\frac{2}{3}$ of £2   **23.** $3\frac{1}{4}$ of 1s.

24. $4\frac{1}{5}$ of 10s.   **25.** $3\frac{3}{16}$ of 1 lb.   **26.** $2\frac{2}{7}$ of 1 cwt.

27. $3\frac{3}{16}$ of 1 cwt. **28.** $5\frac{7}{12}$ of 1 ft. **29.** $4\frac{11}{12}$ of 1 yd.

30. $7\frac{1}{8}$ of 1 day.

ADDITION OF VULGAR FRACTIONS

Example 6. Add together $\frac{2}{3}+\frac{3}{4}+\frac{4}{5}+\frac{5}{6}$.

The L.C.M. of the denominators, 3, 4, 5, 6 = 60

∴ each of the fractions can be expressed with denominator 60.

$$\therefore \frac{2}{3}+\frac{3}{4}+\frac{4}{5}+\frac{5}{6}=\frac{40}{60}+\frac{45}{60}+\frac{48}{60}+\frac{50}{60}$$

$$=\frac{183}{60}$$

$$=3\frac{3}{60}$$

$$=3\frac{1}{20}$$

In actual practice the working is set down as follows:

$$\frac{2}{3}+\frac{3}{4}+\frac{4}{5}+\frac{5}{5}$$

$$=\frac{40+45+48+50}{60}$$

$$=\frac{183}{60}$$

$$=3\frac{3}{60}$$

$$=3\frac{1}{20}$$

The following rules for Addition of Fractions will be useful:

    1. Find the L.C.M. of denominators.
    2. Express each fraction with this L.C.M. as common denominator
    3. Add the numbers in new numerator.
    4. Simplify.

In the Addition of Mixed Numbers:

    1. Add the whole numbers by themselves.
    2. Add the fractions.
    3. Add these two results.

Example 7. Add together $4\frac{1}{3}+5\frac{2}{5}+3\frac{7}{10}$.

$$4\frac{1}{3}+5\frac{2}{5}+3\frac{7}{10}=12+\frac{10+12+21}{30}$$
$$=12\frac{43}{30}$$
$$=13\frac{13}{30}$$

Example 8. Add together $2\frac{3}{4}+3\frac{1}{6}+5\frac{5}{8}+1\frac{9}{12}$.

$$2\frac{3}{4}+3\frac{1}{6}+5\frac{5}{8}+1\frac{9}{12}=2\frac{3}{4}+3\frac{1}{6}+5\frac{5}{8}+1\frac{7}{12}$$
$$=11+\frac{36+8+30+28}{48}$$
$$=11\frac{102}{48}$$
$$=13\frac{6}{48}$$
$$=13\frac{1}{8}$$

EXERCISE 4H. Oral

Add together the following:

  1. $\frac{1}{2}+\frac{1}{3}$ **2.** $\frac{1}{3}+\frac{1}{4}$ **3.** $\frac{2}{3}+\frac{1}{6}$

  4. $\frac{3}{5}+\frac{1}{2}$ **5.** $\frac{3}{4}+\frac{5}{6}$ **6.** $\frac{3}{5}+\frac{7}{8}$

  7. $\frac{1}{3}+\frac{3}{4}+\frac{4}{5}$ **8.** $\frac{1}{6}+\frac{7}{8}+\frac{5}{12}$ **9.** $\frac{3}{5}+\frac{7}{10}+\frac{11}{15}$

10. $\frac{3}{8}+\frac{5}{12}+\frac{9}{16}$ **11.** $1\frac{1}{4}+2\frac{1}{2}$ **12.** $2\frac{1}{3}+1\frac{5}{6}$

13. $3\frac{1}{8}+4\frac{1}{2}$ **14.** $4\frac{1}{5}+5\frac{3}{4}$ **15.** $6\frac{2}{3}+1\frac{1}{4}$

EXERCISE 41

Add together the following:

1. $\frac{3}{4}+\frac{2}{3}$ 2. $\frac{5}{6}+\frac{7}{8}$ 3. $\frac{8}{9}+\frac{11}{12}$

4. $\frac{7}{12}+\frac{13}{18}$ 5. $\frac{11}{15}+\frac{13}{20}$ 6. $\frac{1}{2}+\frac{5}{8}+\frac{7}{12}$

7. $\frac{1}{4}+\frac{2}{5}+\frac{5}{6}$ 8. $\frac{5}{7}+\frac{3}{14}+\frac{13}{28}$ 9. $\frac{4}{5}+\frac{12}{25}+\frac{37}{75}$

10. $\frac{1}{2}+\frac{1}{3}+\frac{1}{4}+\frac{1}{5}$ 11. $\frac{1}{3}+\frac{1}{6}+\frac{1}{9}+\frac{1}{12}$ 12. $\frac{3}{4}+\frac{5}{8}+\frac{7}{12}+\frac{13}{16}$

13. $\frac{3}{4}+\frac{5}{8}+\frac{4}{9}+\frac{7}{12}$ 14. $\frac{1}{3}+\frac{3}{5}+\frac{7}{8}+\frac{9}{10}$ 15. $\frac{7}{12}+\frac{11}{16}+\frac{13}{18}+\frac{19}{36}$

16. $1\frac{5}{6}+2\frac{3}{4}$ 17. $2\frac{2}{3}+3\frac{7}{8}$ 18. $3\frac{7}{9}+1\frac{8}{15}$

19. $4\frac{7}{12}+5\frac{13}{20}$ 20. $3\frac{11}{18}+\frac{67}{12}$ 21. $2\frac{1}{2}+3\frac{3}{8}+1\frac{5}{12}$

22. $2\frac{3}{4}+5\frac{4}{5}+1\frac{1}{6}$ 23. $4\frac{5}{7}+5\frac{11}{16}+3\frac{3}{4}$ 24. $2\frac{2}{5}+5\frac{7}{10}+\frac{53}{25}$

25. $1\frac{1}{2}+3\frac{2}{3}+4\frac{1}{4}+1\frac{3}{5}$ 26. $2\frac{1}{3}+1\frac{5}{6}+3\frac{7}{9}+5\frac{5}{12}$

27. $5\frac{3}{4}+1\frac{7}{8}+2\frac{11}{12}+3\frac{11}{16}$ 28. $7\frac{1}{4}+2\frac{3}{8}+3\frac{7}{9}+5\frac{5}{12}$

29. $1\frac{17}{30}+2\frac{2}{5}+4\frac{5}{8}+3\frac{7}{10}$ 30. $\frac{19}{12}+2\frac{7}{16}+3\frac{11}{18}+1\frac{13}{36}$

SUBTRACTION OF VULGAR FRACTIONS

The method for subtraction is exactly the same as for addition, but careful attention should be given to worked example No. 11 which follows.

Example 9. Subtract $\frac{7}{12}$ from $\frac{5}{8}$.

$$\frac{5}{8}-\frac{7}{12}$$

$$=\frac{15-14}{24}$$

$$=\frac{1}{24}$$

Example 10. From $3\frac{15}{16}$ take $1\frac{7}{10}$.

$$3\frac{15}{16}-1\frac{7}{10}$$

$$=2+\frac{75-56}{80}$$

$$=2\frac{19}{80}$$

Example 11. Subtract $4\frac{5}{8}$ from $7\frac{7}{18}$.

$$7\tfrac{7}{18} - 4\tfrac{5}{8}$$

$$= 3 + \frac{28 - 45}{72}$$

$$= 2 + \frac{72 + 28 - 45}{72} \qquad \ldots \ldots \text{(A)}$$

$$= 2\frac{100 - 45}{72}$$

$$= 2\frac{55}{72}$$

Note that in Example 11, line (A), one unit has been converted to $\frac{72}{72}$ so that the subtraction impossible in the previous line might take place.

EXERCISE 4J. *Oral*

Subtract:

1. $\frac{1}{2} - \frac{1}{3}$	**2.** $\frac{2}{3} - \frac{1}{4}$	**3.** $\frac{3}{5} - \frac{1}{6}$	**4.** $\frac{5}{6} - \frac{3}{4}$
5. $\frac{7}{8} - \frac{4}{5}$	**6.** $\frac{7}{12} - \frac{3}{8}$	**7.** $\frac{11}{15} - \frac{7}{10}$	**8.** $\frac{7}{8} - \frac{5}{12}$
9. $2\frac{2}{3} - 1\frac{1}{4}$	**10.** $3\frac{5}{8} - 1\frac{3}{5}$	**11.** $6\frac{8}{15} - 2\frac{3}{10}$	**12.** $8\frac{5}{12} - 3\frac{3}{8}$
13. $9\frac{7}{8} - 5\frac{5}{6}$	**14.** $10\frac{11}{15} - 7\frac{17}{20}$	**15.** $10\frac{8}{9} - 7\frac{11}{12}$	

EXERCISE 4K

Subtract:

1. $5 - 3\frac{3}{8}$	**2.** $4 - 2\frac{5}{7}$	**3.** $6\frac{7}{8} - 1\frac{5}{12}$
4. $8\frac{5}{6} - 5\frac{3}{4}$	**5.** $7\frac{7}{10} - 4\frac{17}{25}$	**6.** $10\frac{11}{16} - 6\frac{7}{24}$
7. $14\frac{7}{15} - 9\frac{3}{20}$	**8.** $17\frac{17}{18} - 13\frac{23}{30}$	**9.** $18\frac{21}{25} - 14\frac{31}{45}$
10. $7\frac{7}{10} - 4\frac{17}{20}$	**11.** $6\frac{9}{16} - 3\frac{19}{24}$	**12.** $9\frac{11}{18} - 5\frac{13}{15}$

13. By how much is $13\frac{13}{25}$ greater than $8\frac{11}{15}$?

14. By how much is $12\frac{13}{16}$ less than $16\frac{11}{18}$?

15. Which is greater and by how much: $4\frac{1}{12}$ or $2\frac{13}{14}$?

16. From $6\frac{33}{49}$ take $5\frac{52}{77}$.

17. From $7\frac{13}{21}$ take $4\frac{17}{28}$.

18. Subtract $7\frac{7}{16}$ from $8\frac{5}{9}$.

19. Find the difference between $9\frac{11}{15}$ and $7\frac{7}{12}$.

20. Find the difference between $14\frac{17}{21}$ and $19\frac{25}{48}$.

Example 12. Simplify $5\frac{5}{12}+3\frac{4}{9}-2\frac{5}{6}-4\frac{7}{8}$.

$$5\frac{5}{12}+3\frac{4}{9}-2\frac{5}{6}-4\frac{7}{8}$$

$$=2+\frac{30+32-60-63}{72}$$

$$=2\frac{62-123}{72}$$

$$=1\frac{134-123}{72}$$

$$=1\frac{11}{72}$$

EXERCISE 4L

Simplify the following:

1. $2\frac{2}{3}+4\frac{1}{4}-5\frac{1}{2}$

2. $5\frac{1}{4}+2\frac{1}{8}-3\frac{2}{3}$

3. $4\frac{1}{4}-3\frac{2}{5}+2\frac{5}{6}$

4. $3\frac{2}{7}+4\frac{5}{21}-2\frac{13}{14}$

5. $5\frac{5}{7}+7\frac{3}{14}-9\frac{13}{28}$

6. $8\frac{3}{5}-3\frac{7}{10}-2\frac{13}{25}$

7. $6\frac{5}{7}-5\frac{11}{16}+4\frac{3}{4}$

8. $7\frac{7}{12}+4\frac{9}{16}-5\frac{13}{20}$

9. $11\frac{13}{18}-4\frac{17}{24}-3\frac{19}{27}$

10. $12\frac{17}{24}-10\frac{15}{32}+7\frac{19}{36}$

11. $2\frac{1}{2}+3\frac{2}{3}-4\frac{1}{4}+1\frac{3}{5}$

12. $2\frac{1}{3}-1\frac{5}{6}-3\frac{7}{9}+5\frac{5}{12}$

13. $5\frac{3}{4}+1\frac{7}{18}-2\frac{11}{12}-3\frac{11}{16}$

14. $3\frac{1}{4}-4\frac{5}{6}-\frac{11}{12}+2\frac{3}{5}$

15. $3\frac{7}{12}+2\frac{9}{16}-3\frac{11}{18}+1\frac{17}{36}$

16. From the sum of $2\frac{2}{3}+1\frac{1}{2}+4\frac{3}{8}$ take $6\frac{1}{4}$.

17. Add together $3\frac{3}{5}-1\frac{3}{4}$ and $4\frac{1}{3}-2\frac{5}{12}$.

18. Subtract $5\frac{7}{8}+2\frac{5}{9}$ from $12\frac{17}{18}-1\frac{2}{3}$.

19. By how much is 7 greater than $4\frac{7}{12}+1\frac{19}{42}$?

20. Which is greater and by how much, $3\frac{7}{8}+2\frac{13}{18}$ or $2\frac{3}{8}+3\frac{17}{18}$?

21. What must be added to $3\frac{11}{12}+4\frac{17}{18}$ to make $9\frac{23}{24}$?

22. What must be subtracted from 9 to leave $2\frac{13}{15}+4\frac{17}{20}$?

23. From the sum of $3\frac{6}{7}$ and $2\frac{2}{3}$ take the difference of $4\frac{17}{21}$ and $1\frac{1}{2}$.

24. To the difference of $7\frac{7}{8}$ and $3\frac{9}{10}$ add the sum of $1\frac{15}{16}$ and $2\frac{19}{40}$.

25. What number subtracted from $9\frac{31}{72}$ will give the same result as that obtained by adding $3\frac{17}{36}$ and $4\frac{5}{8}$?

MULTIPLICATION OF VULGAR FRACTIONS

(A) By a **whole number**

Example 13. Multiply $\frac{3}{4}$ by 5.

$\frac{3}{4} \times 5$ means $\frac{3}{4}+\frac{3}{4}+\frac{3}{4}+\frac{3}{4}+\frac{3}{4}$ where $\frac{3}{4}$ is repeated 5 times

$$\text{Hence } \frac{3}{4} \times 5 = \frac{15}{4}$$

$$= 3\tfrac{3}{4}$$

Note that this same result is obtained by

(i) multiplying the numerator 3 by 5

and then   (ii) dividing the result 15 by 4.

Example 14. Multiply $\frac{4}{5}$ by 7.

$$\frac{4}{5} \times 7$$
$$= \frac{28}{5}$$
$$= 5\tfrac{3}{5}$$

Example 15. Multiply $1\frac{5}{6}$ by 12.
Consider the following three methods:

(i) $1\frac{5}{6} \times 12 = \dfrac{11}{6} \times 12 = \dfrac{132}{6} = 22$

(ii) $1\frac{5}{6} \times 12 = \dfrac{11 \times \overset{2*}{\cancel{12}}}{\underset{1}{\cancel{6}}} = 22$

(iii) $1\frac{5}{6} \times 12 = 12 + \frac{5}{6} \times 12 = 12 + 10 = 22$

* In method (ii) the numerator and denominator are divided by a common factor 6 and this simplifies the expression considerably.

This process of dividing numerator and denominator by a common factor is frequently referred to as 'cancelling', and when the original numbers are stroked out and new ones inserted the 'cancelling factor' is usually self-evident.

EXERCISE 4M

Multiply:

1. $\frac{3}{5}$ by 4	**2.** $\frac{4}{7}$ by 5	**3.** $\frac{5}{6}$ by 7
4. $\frac{2}{3}$ by 6	**5.** $\frac{3}{4}$ by 12	**6.** $\frac{7}{8}$ by 18
7. $1\frac{2}{5}$ by 7	**8.** $2\frac{3}{7}$ by 4	**9.** $3\frac{5}{6}$ by 5
	10. $2\frac{2}{3}$ by 12	

Simplify:

11. $\frac{31}{36} \times 12$	**12.** $\frac{43}{50} \times 10$	**13.** $\frac{53}{72} \times 9$
14. $3\frac{3}{4} \times 6$	**15.** $4\frac{7}{8} \times 24$	**16.** $2\frac{3}{21} \times 7$
17. $4\frac{17}{42} \times 14$	**18.** $5\frac{7}{33} \times 11$	**19.** $3\frac{27}{56} \times 16$
	20. $7\frac{11}{12} \times 24$	

(B) By a **fraction**

Consider diagram I as representing a block of chocolate. Then three-quarters $(\frac{3}{4})$ of the block is indicated by the shaded portion.

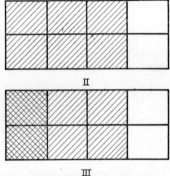

We can think of this shaded portion as being divided into six equal parts, and one-third $(\frac{1}{3})$ of this portion is indicated by the double shading. That is, one-third $(\frac{1}{3})$ of three-quarters $(\frac{3}{4})$ of the block is equal to one-quarter $(\frac{1}{4})$ of the block (see diagram II).

It is an easy step to understand that two-thirds $(\frac{2}{3})$ of three-quarters $(\frac{3}{4})$ of the block will be twice this amount, namely, one-half $(\frac{1}{2})$ of the block (see diagram III).

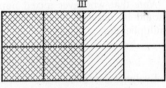

Abbreviating all this work, we arrive at this conclusion that

$\frac{2}{3}$ of $\frac{3}{4}$ of a block of chocolate $= \frac{1}{2}$ of a block

Considering only the arithmetic of this problem, we have

$$\frac{2}{3} \text{ of } \frac{3}{4} = \frac{2}{3} \times \frac{3}{4} = \frac{\overset{1}{2} \times \overset{1}{3}}{\underset{1}{3} \times \underset{2}{4}} = \frac{1}{2}$$

This multiplication $\frac{2}{3} \times \frac{3}{4}$ may be done more quickly thus, $\dfrac{\overset{1}{2}}{\underset{1}{3}} \times \dfrac{\overset{1}{3}}{\underset{2}{4}} = \frac{1}{2}$,

where in turn we divide the numerator of one fraction and the

denominator of the other by 2 and then the remaining numerator and denominator by 3.

Example 16. Multiply $\frac{4}{5}$ by $\frac{25}{32}$.

$$\frac{4}{5} \times \frac{25}{32} = \overset{1}{\underset{1}{\frac{4}{5}}} \times \overset{5}{\underset{8}{\frac{25}{32}}} = \frac{5}{8}$$

Example 17. Find $\frac{3}{4}$ of $2\frac{2}{9}$.

$$\frac{3}{4} \text{ of } 2\frac{2}{9} = \overset{1}{\underset{1}{\frac{3}{4}}} \times \overset{5}{\underset{3}{\frac{20}{9}}} = 1\frac{2}{3}$$

Example 18. Multiply $4\frac{1}{6}$ by $3\frac{1}{5}$.

$$4\frac{1}{6} \times 3\frac{1}{5} = \overset{5}{\underset{3}{\frac{25}{6}}} \times \overset{8}{\underset{1}{\frac{16}{5}}} = \frac{40}{3} = 13\frac{1}{3}$$

Note that whenever mixed numbers appear in a question, these should be reduced to improper fractions before proceeding with multiplication.

EXERCISE 4N. *Oral*

Evaluate the following:

1. $\frac{1}{2} \times \frac{1}{3}$ 2. $\frac{1}{3} \times \frac{1}{4}$ 3. $\frac{1}{2} \times \frac{2}{3}$ 4. $\frac{1}{3} \times \frac{3}{4}$
5. $\frac{1}{4} \times \frac{4}{5}$ 6. $\frac{1}{5} \times \frac{5}{6}$ 7. $\frac{3}{4} \times \frac{4}{5}$ 8. $\frac{4}{5} \times \frac{5}{6}$
9. $\frac{5}{6} \times \frac{9}{10}$ 10. $\frac{5}{6} \times \frac{14}{15}$ 11. $\frac{1}{2} \times 1\frac{1}{3}$ 12. $\frac{1}{3} \times 2\frac{1}{4}$
13. $\frac{1}{4} \times 3\frac{1}{5}$ 14. $\frac{2}{3} \times 2\frac{2}{5}$ 15. $\frac{4}{5} \times 3\frac{3}{4}$ 16. $\frac{3}{4}$ of $2\frac{5}{9}$
17. $\frac{5}{6}$ of $4\frac{1}{5}$ 18. $1\frac{1}{2}$ of $2\frac{2}{3}$ 19. $3\frac{3}{4}$ of $1\frac{3}{5}$ 20. $5\frac{5}{6}$ of $2\frac{7}{10}$

EXERCISE 4O

Evaluate the following:

1. $1\frac{7}{9} \times \frac{3}{7} \times 2\frac{5}{8}$ 2. $4\frac{1}{4} \times 5\frac{1}{5} \times 1\frac{3}{17}$
3. $3\frac{1}{5} \times 4\frac{2}{7} \times 5\frac{5}{13}$ 4. $3\frac{2}{3} \times 5\frac{1}{9} \times \frac{27}{46}$
5. $4\frac{2}{3} \times 1\frac{2}{7} \times 5\frac{5}{6}$ 6. $4\frac{1}{5} \times 2\frac{1}{7} \times \frac{13}{27} \times 1\frac{1}{26}$

7. $4\frac{5}{8} \times 1\frac{29}{35} \times 3\frac{1}{2} \times 1\frac{3}{37}$ **8.** $2\frac{1}{9} \times \frac{3}{7} \times \frac{15}{38} \times 2\frac{1}{5}$

9. $3\frac{2}{5} \times \frac{25}{34} \times 5\frac{1}{3} \times 2\frac{1}{4}$ **10.** $3\frac{6}{7} \times 1\frac{5}{9} \times \frac{3}{10} \times 6\frac{2}{3}$

11. $4\frac{1}{3} \times \frac{27}{32}$ of $4\frac{7}{26}$ **12.** $1\frac{1}{4}$ of $3\frac{1}{5} \times 1\frac{3}{8}$

13. $2\frac{1}{7}$ of $4\frac{1}{5}$ of $1\frac{1}{9}$ **14.** $4\frac{1}{3}$ of $1\frac{4}{5}$ of $\frac{20}{39}$

15. $5\frac{2}{3}$ of $\frac{11}{51} \times 1\frac{7}{11}$

DIVISION OF VULGAR FRACTIONS

(A) By a **whole number**

Suppose we have a whole block of chocolate to be divided equally between three people.

Then each person will receive one-third ($\frac{1}{3}$) of a block.

Hence, dividing by 3 is equivalent to taking $\frac{1}{3}$ of the quantity.

If, in the first instance, we have only three-quarters ($\frac{3}{4}$) of a block of chocolate to be divided equally between three people, each person will now receive

$$\frac{3}{4} \div 3 \quad or \quad \frac{3}{4 \times 3} \quad or \quad \frac{1}{4} \text{ of a block}$$

We can think of this problem again as finding one-third ($\frac{1}{3}$) of three-quarters ($\frac{3}{4}$), that is

$$\frac{1}{3} \text{ of } \frac{3}{4} = \frac{1}{\underset{1}{\cancel{3}}} \times \frac{\overset{1}{\cancel{3}}}{4} = \frac{1}{4}$$

RULE. To divide a fraction by a whole number, then, multiply the denominator of the fraction by that number and simplify.

Example 19. Divide $3\frac{1}{4}$ by 3.

$$3\frac{1}{4} \div 3 = \frac{13}{4} \div 3 = \frac{13}{4 \times 3} = \frac{13}{12} = 1\frac{1}{12}$$

Example 20. Divide $4\frac{1}{5}$ by 7.

$$4\frac{1}{5} \div 7 = \frac{21}{5} \div 7 = \frac{\overset{3}{\cancel{21}}}{5 \times \underset{1}{\cancel{7}}} = \frac{3}{5}$$

(B) By a **fraction**

Consider the example $56 \div 8 = 7$.

This example may be done by answering the question,

'What number multiplied by 8 gives 56?'

In the same way in dealing with the example $1 \div \frac{3}{4}$ we ask ourselves,

'What number multiplied by $\frac{3}{4}$ gives 1?'

and the answer is evidently $\frac{4}{3}$, i.e. $1\frac{1}{3}$.

Hence, division by $\frac{3}{4}$ may be regarded as multiplication by the reciprocal of this number, namely, $\frac{4}{3}$.

This may be clearer from a consideration of the following example.

Example 21. Divide $\frac{4}{5}$ by $\frac{2}{3}$.

$$\frac{\frac{4}{5}}{\frac{2}{3}} = \frac{\overset{1}{\cancel{\frac{4}{5}}} \times \overset{1}{\cancel{5}} \times 3}{\frac{2}{\cancel{3}} \times 5 \times \cancel{3}_1} = \frac{4 \times 3}{2 \times 5} = \frac{\overset{2}{\cancel{4}}}{5} \times \frac{3}{\cancel{2}_1} = \frac{6}{5} = 1\frac{1}{5}$$

When the two parts linked together are examined the following result emerges.

RULE. To divide any number by a fraction, multiply by the reciprocal of the fraction *or* In division by a fraction, turn the divisor upside down and multiply.

Note two further points:

1. In Example 21 instead of $\frac{4}{5} \div \frac{2}{3}$, the question has been written $\frac{\frac{4}{5}}{\frac{2}{3}}$, where the longer horizontal line replaces the division sign.

2. In division examples involving mixed numbers, these should first be expressed as improper fractions.

Example 22. Divide $4\frac{1}{6}$ by $\frac{5}{9}$.

$$4\frac{1}{6} \div \frac{5}{9} = \frac{25}{6} \div \frac{5}{9} = \frac{\overset{5}{\cancel{25}}}{\cancel{6}_2} \times \frac{\overset{3}{\cancel{9}}}{\cancel{5}_1} = \frac{15}{2} = 7\frac{1}{2}$$

Example 23. Divide $2\frac{7}{10}$ by $1\frac{1}{8}$.

$$2\frac{7}{10} \div 1\frac{1}{8} = \frac{27}{10} \div \frac{9}{8} = \frac{\overset{3}{\cancel{27}}}{\cancel{10}_5} \times \frac{\overset{4}{\cancel{8}}}{\cancel{9}_1} = \frac{12}{5} = 2\frac{2}{5}$$

Divide the following:

1. $\frac{8}{9} \div 4$ 2. $\frac{9}{10} \div 3$ 3. $1\frac{7}{8} \div 5$

4. $2\frac{4}{5} \div 7$ 5. $3\frac{3}{8} \div 9$ 6. $\frac{1}{6} \div \frac{1}{3}$

7. $\frac{1}{12} \div \frac{1}{4}$ 8. $\frac{1}{3} \div \frac{1}{2}$ 9. $\frac{3}{5} \div \frac{3}{4}$

10. $\frac{2}{3} \div \frac{5}{6}$ 11. $\frac{2}{3} \div \frac{1}{2}$ 12. $\frac{3}{4} \div \frac{1}{3}$

13. $\frac{4}{5} \div 3\frac{1}{5}$ 14. $1\frac{3}{5} \div \frac{2}{3}$ 15. $1\frac{11}{12} \div \frac{3}{4}$

Divide the following:

1. $3 \div 3\frac{3}{4}$ 2. $4 \div 2\frac{2}{3}$ 3. $6 \div 1\frac{3}{5}$

4. $3\frac{1}{2} \div 4\frac{1}{5}$ 5. $15\frac{3}{4} \div 5\frac{5}{6}$ 6. $2\frac{2}{3} \div \frac{4}{5}$

7. $2\frac{1}{4} \div 2\frac{1}{7}$ 8. $2\frac{7}{9} \div 4\frac{3}{8}$ 9. $7\frac{1}{3} \div 5\frac{5}{7}$

10. $8\frac{2}{5} \div 4\frac{1}{5}$ 11. $8\frac{1}{10} \div 3\frac{3}{8}$ 12. $11\frac{2}{3} \div 1\frac{23}{27}$

13. $8\frac{3}{4} \div 4\frac{3}{8}$ 14. $16\frac{1}{5} \div 40\frac{1}{2}$ 15. $14\frac{4}{7} \div 20\frac{2}{5}$

16. $40\frac{5}{9} \div 60\frac{5}{6}$ 17. $16\frac{6}{11} \div 8\frac{2}{3}$ 18. $31\frac{5}{13} \div 14\frac{4}{7}$

19. $1\frac{14}{121} \div 2\frac{2}{11}$ 20. $2\frac{1}{42} \div 3\frac{9}{14}$

SIMPLIFICATION OF VULGAR FRACTIONS

Thus far we have considered only examples in which ONE or at the most TWO processes were involved, and in the latter case these processes were connected, e.g. '+' and '−'; 'of' and '×'.

Let us now establish one or two simple rules by referring to specific types of example.

Example 24. Simplify $5\frac{1}{2} + 3\frac{1}{3} \times 4\frac{1}{5}$.

In this example the '×' sign takes priority over the '+' sign.

Thus
$$5\frac{1}{2} + 3\frac{1}{3} \times 4\frac{1}{5}$$

$$= 5\frac{1}{2} + \left(\frac{\overset{2}{\cancel{10}}}{\underset{1}{\cancel{3}}} \times \frac{\overset{7}{\cancel{21}}}{\underset{1}{\cancel{5}}} \right)$$

$$= 5\frac{1}{2} + 14$$

$$= 19\frac{1}{2}$$

Notice that the multiplication operation can be isolated by the use of brackets.

Example 25. Simplify $4\frac{1}{4}-3\frac{1}{5}\times\frac{5}{8}+3\frac{5}{16}$.

Again the two quantities connected by the '$\times$' sign should be dealt with first.

Hence
$$4\frac{1}{4}-3\frac{1}{5}\times\frac{5}{8}+3\frac{5}{16}$$
$$=4\frac{1}{4}-\left(\frac{\overset{2}{\cancel{16}}}{\cancel{5}}\times\frac{\cancel{5}}{\cancel{8}}\right)+3\frac{5}{16}$$
$$=4\frac{1}{4}-2+3\frac{5}{16}$$
$$=2\frac{1}{4}+3\frac{5}{16}$$
$$=5\frac{4+5}{16}$$
$$=5\frac{9}{16}$$

Example 26. Simplify $3\frac{3}{7}\div5\frac{5}{7}$ of $\frac{7}{32}-2\frac{2}{7}$.

In this example the operations are dealt with in the order 'of', '$\div$' and '$-$'.

Thus
$$3\frac{3}{7}\div5\frac{5}{7} \text{ of } \frac{7}{32}-2\frac{2}{7}$$
$$=3\frac{3}{7}\div\left(\frac{\overset{5}{\cancel{40}}}{\cancel{7}}\times\frac{\cancel{7}}{\cancel{32}}\right)-2\frac{2}{7}$$
$$=3\frac{3}{7}\div1\frac{1}{4}-2\frac{2}{7}$$
$$=\left(\frac{24}{7}\times\frac{4}{5}\right)-2\frac{2}{7}$$
$$=\frac{96}{35}-2\frac{2}{7}$$
$$=2\frac{26}{35}-2\frac{2}{7}$$
$$=\frac{26-10}{35}$$
$$=\frac{16}{35}$$

Example 27. Simplify $2\frac{3}{4}\div5\frac{1}{2}\times3\frac{1}{3}$.

In this example the '$\div$' and '$\times$' signs affect only the numbers immediately following them.

Thus
$$2\tfrac{3}{4} \div 5\tfrac{1}{2} \times 3\tfrac{1}{3}$$

$$= \frac{\overset{1}{\cancel{11}}}{\underset{2}{\cancel{4}}} \times \frac{\overset{1}{\cancel{2}}}{\cancel{11}} \times \frac{\overset{5}{\cancel{10}}}{3}$$
$$\underset{1}{}$$

$$= \frac{5}{3}$$

$$= 1\tfrac{2}{3}$$

In complicated simplification of fractions it will be found useful to follow this order of priority:

1. Brackets and 'of'
2. '÷' and '×'
3. '+' and '−'

EXERCISE 4R

Simplify the following:

1. $\dfrac{3\tfrac{2}{3}+4\tfrac{1}{4}}{9\tfrac{1}{2}\times 3\tfrac{1}{3}}$

2. $(6\tfrac{3}{8}-3\tfrac{2}{3})\div 5\tfrac{1}{2}$

3. $\tfrac{5}{42}+\tfrac{4}{9}$ of $\tfrac{3}{7}$

4. $\dfrac{16\tfrac{2}{3}}{18\tfrac{3}{4}}\div\dfrac{80}{81}$

5. $6\tfrac{3}{10}-5\tfrac{4}{9}+(3\tfrac{1}{3}+2\tfrac{1}{2})$

✓**6.** $\dfrac{3\tfrac{1}{2}+2\tfrac{1}{4}+1\tfrac{1}{5}}{4\tfrac{1}{2}+2\tfrac{1}{3}-1\tfrac{1}{6}}$

7. $(1\tfrac{7}{8}+2\tfrac{2}{5})\div(\tfrac{3}{14}\times 4\tfrac{1}{5})$

8. $4\tfrac{1}{5}\times 5\tfrac{2}{3}\div 3\tfrac{2}{3}$

9. $(\tfrac{2}{5}$ of $\tfrac{3}{7})\div(\tfrac{4}{5}-\tfrac{3}{7})$

10. $(4\tfrac{1}{3}+1\tfrac{3}{4}-2\tfrac{5}{6})\div 1\tfrac{1}{12}$ of $2\tfrac{1}{7}$

11. $(\tfrac{1}{4}+\tfrac{5}{18})\div(6\tfrac{1}{4}-1\tfrac{2}{5}\times 3\tfrac{1}{3})$

12. $(\tfrac{7}{8}-\tfrac{1}{5})\div\{\tfrac{3}{8}\times(1\tfrac{3}{5}-\tfrac{1}{4})\}$

13. $\dfrac{1\tfrac{3}{8}+3\tfrac{1}{3}-\tfrac{5}{7}}{\tfrac{3}{4}+\tfrac{1}{7}}$

14. $1\tfrac{1}{4}+\tfrac{3}{7}$ of $5\tfrac{5}{6}-3\tfrac{4}{7}\div 1\tfrac{1}{4}$

15. $(6\tfrac{1}{2}$ of $5\tfrac{1}{11})-2\tfrac{1}{6}\div(\tfrac{2}{3}$ of $3\tfrac{1}{4})$

16. $3\tfrac{1}{2}+\tfrac{1}{3}$ of $2\tfrac{1}{4}-\tfrac{4}{5}\div 1\tfrac{1}{3}$

17. $\dfrac{6\tfrac{1}{4}-2\tfrac{1}{2}\div 1\tfrac{1}{2}}{1\tfrac{3}{8}\times 1\tfrac{1}{3}+1\tfrac{4}{7}}$

18. $\dfrac{1\tfrac{2}{3}}{\tfrac{5}{13} \text{ of } 4\tfrac{1}{3}}-\tfrac{5}{9}$ of $\dfrac{3\tfrac{1}{2}}{1\tfrac{17}{18}}$

19. $\dfrac{5\tfrac{3}{4}-2\tfrac{1}{2}\div 3\tfrac{1}{3}}{(5\tfrac{3}{4}-2\tfrac{1}{2})+3\tfrac{1}{3}}$

20. $\dfrac{3\tfrac{4}{7}\times 2\tfrac{2}{5}}{3\tfrac{4}{7}-2\tfrac{2}{5}}\times 5\tfrac{6}{7}$

21. $\dfrac{3\tfrac{1}{2}-1\tfrac{1}{8}}{\tfrac{5}{6}+2\tfrac{1}{3}}\times(3\tfrac{3}{7}-2\tfrac{5}{14})$

22. $\dfrac{5\tfrac{1}{4}-4\tfrac{1}{3}}{5\tfrac{1}{3}+4\tfrac{1}{6}}\div\tfrac{7}{25}$

23. $\dfrac{2\frac{1}{2}+3\frac{1}{4}\div\frac{4}{5}\text{ of }\frac{13}{20}}{(2\frac{1}{3}+1\frac{3}{4})\times2\frac{4}{7}-5\frac{1}{4}}$ **24.** $\dfrac{2\frac{1}{2}-1\frac{1}{6}\div(\frac{3}{4}+\frac{11}{12})}{\frac{3}{4}-(\frac{7}{8}-\frac{3}{4})+\frac{9}{10}}$

25. $\dfrac{\frac{2}{5}-\frac{2}{3}\text{ of }\frac{2}{5}}{3\frac{3}{5}-1\frac{3}{5}\text{ of }1\frac{3}{7}-\frac{3}{7}}\times4\frac{3}{7}$

26. Multiply $3\frac{1}{2}+5\frac{1}{4}-2\frac{1}{3}$ by $4\frac{1}{11}+2\frac{1}{2}-1\frac{3}{22}$.

27. Find the difference between $6\frac{1}{2}\times4\frac{3}{4}$ and $4\frac{1}{4}\times3\frac{1}{8}$.

28. Find the value of $\frac{3}{5}$ of £2 15s. 5d. $+\frac{4}{7}$ of £1 19s. 8d. $-\frac{5}{9}$ of £3 6s. 9d.

29. Evaluate $\frac{3}{4}$ of 7s. 6d. $+2\frac{1}{2}$ of 10s. 5d. $-\frac{2}{3}$ of £1 15s.

30. (a) Find the difference between $\frac{5}{6}$ of £2 10s. and $\frac{10}{11}$ of £1 7s. 6d.

     (b) Find the value of $\frac{5}{8}$ of £4 8s.

     (c) What fraction is the answer in (a) of the answer in (b)?

PROBLEMS INVOLVING VULGAR FRACTIONS

Example 28. A man loses $\frac{3}{5}$ of his capital one year and $\frac{1}{4}$ of what remains the next year. He has £270. What was his original capital?

Fraction of original capital lost in 1st year
$$=\tfrac{3}{5}$$

∴   „   „   „   „   remaining at end of 1st year
$$=\tfrac{2}{5}$$

∴   „   „   „   „   lost in 2nd year
$$=\tfrac{1}{4}\text{ of }\tfrac{2}{5}=\frac{1}{\underset{2}{4}}\times\frac{\overset{1}{2}}{5}=\tfrac{1}{10}$$

∴   „   „   „   „   remaining at end of 2nd year
$$=\tfrac{2}{5}-\tfrac{1}{10}=\tfrac{3}{10}$$

But capital remaining at end of 2nd year
$$=£270$$

∴ $\frac{3}{10}$ of original capital $=£270$

∴ Original capital $=£\overset{90}{\cancel{270}}\times\dfrac{\overset{10}{\cancel{10}}}{\underset{1}{\cancel{3}}}$

$$=£900$$

OR

Let original capital $= £x$

$\therefore$ Amount lost in 1st year $= £\frac{3}{5}x$

$\therefore$ „ remaining at end of 1st year $= £\frac{2}{5}x$

$\therefore$ Amount lost in 2nd year $= \frac{1}{4}$ of $£\frac{2}{5}x = £\frac{1}{10}x$

$\therefore$ „ remaining at end of 2nd year $= £(\frac{2}{5}x - \frac{1}{10}x) = £\frac{3}{10}x$

$$\therefore £\tfrac{3}{10}x = £270$$
$$\therefore x = 900$$
$$\therefore \text{Original capital} = £900$$

Note that detailed working should be set down in **all** problems. A mass of figures and fractions and a final result do not constitute a full solution of the problem.

EXERCISE 4s

1. A boy has 4s. 8d.; what fraction of this is left after he has spent 3s. 4d.?

2. After a girl has spent $\frac{5}{9}$ of her money she has 6s. left; how much had she at first?

3. One box contains $\frac{5}{7}$ of 1 cwt. of flour and another contains $\frac{11}{16}$ of 1 cwt. Find which box contains most flour, and how many lb. it contains more than the other.

4. Three men paid a bill of £5 7s. 11d. If the first paid $\frac{2}{5}$ and the second $\frac{2}{7}$ of it, how much did the third pay in £ s. d.?

5. How many pieces $1\frac{3}{5}$ in. long can be cut from a stick $1\frac{1}{3}$ yd. long?

6. If $\frac{7}{11}$ of an estate is worth £4,655, what is the value of half of the remainder?

7. A cargo of coal is shared by A, B, C and D. A receives $\frac{1}{3}$ of it; B and C each receive $\frac{4}{15}$ of it; D receives 80 tons. How many tons were in the cargo?

8. At a concert, $\frac{4}{9}$ of the audience had 1s. tickets, $\frac{5}{12}$ of the audience had 1s. 6d. tickets, and the remainder, 60 people, had 2s. tickets. How many people were present at the concert and how much money was taken?

9. At a concert, $\frac{1}{6}$ of the people paid 2s. 6d. each for admission, $\frac{1}{5}$ of them paid a florin each, and $\frac{1}{3}$ paid 1s. 3d. each. The remainder, 180 people, paid £4 10s. in all. How many people attended the concert and what were the total drawings?

10. $\frac{2}{5}$ of a sum of money was spent on groceries and $\frac{2}{7}$ on bread and 5s. 6d. was left. What was the original sum of money?

11. The first line of an army consists of $\frac{5}{12}$ of the whole force and the second line of $\frac{2}{5}$ of the whole force. If the remainder numbers 1,210, how many soldiers are there in the whole army?

12. A greengrocer buys 60 lb. of apples at 10d. per lb. He sells $\frac{1}{2}$ of them at 1s. 3d. per lb., $\frac{2}{3}$ of the remainder at 1s. per lb. and the rest at 9d. per lb. What is his total profit?

13. A man used $\frac{1}{5}$ of a length of rope in doing one job and then used $\frac{2}{3}$ of what was left on another job and then found that he had 2 ft. 8 in. of rope left. How many yards of rope did he have to begin with?

14. A boy, after giving $\frac{1}{4}$ of his pocket-money to one companion and $\frac{7}{8}$ of the remainder to another, has 9d. left. How much had he at first?

15. A man spent $\frac{1}{5}$ of a sum of money in paying a bill. He spent $\frac{5}{9}$ of what was left in paying another bill, and then found that he had £16 left. What sum of money had he at first?

16. $\frac{1}{5}$ of an account was paid in cash, $\frac{3}{8}$ of the remainder a month later and the amount still to be paid was £9 15s. What was the amount of the account?

17. A man, after spending $\frac{1}{5}$ of his money on railway fares and $\frac{7}{9}$ of the remainder on other purchases, had 4s. 8d. left. How much had he at first?

18. A man spent half of his money on clothing. He put half of what was over in the bank and gave in charity half of what was now left. He still had £2 10s. How much had he at first?

19. The gate money drawn at a football match was divided equally between the two clubs playing. One of the clubs retained $\frac{5}{8}$ of its share and divided the remainder equally among the 11 players. If each player received £12 6s., how much money was drawn for admission to the match?

20. Going on holiday a man paid $\frac{1}{6}$ of his money for railway fares, $\frac{7}{12}$ of the remainder for board and lodgings and his other expenses were $1\frac{1}{2}$ times the cost of his railway fare. If he brought back £2 4s. 4d., how much money had he when he set out?

5

Decimal Fractions

In the previous chapter we have dealt with Vulgar or Common Fractions; now we are to deal with those fractions associated with the '10' or *decimal* system. This system enables us to extend the traditional way of looking at a number downwards beyond the units level.

We are familiar with such a number as 3,596 written

th.	hund.	tens	units
3	5	9	6

but this idea is now taken further to include tenths, hundredths, thousandths, etc.

Consider the following number expressed in columnar notation:

thousands	hundreds	tens	units	tenths	hundredths	thousandths
2	7	6	1	5	8	4

At the place of transition where we pass from whole numbers (units) to fractions (tenths) there is introduced what is called a '*decimal point*' so that the number we have just expressed would be written 2,761·584. In this number the fractional part may be expressed in detail thus:

$$5 \text{ tenths} + 8 \text{ hundredths} + 4 \text{ thousandths} \quad . \quad . \quad (1)$$
or $\qquad\qquad\qquad 58 \text{ hundredths} + 4 \text{ thousandths}$
or $\qquad\qquad\qquad\qquad\qquad 584 \text{ thousandths}$

From (1) we can see that

5 tenths is written 0·5	and so	1 tenth	is written 0·1;
8 hundredths ,, ,, 0·08	,, ,,	1 hundredth ,,	,, 0·01;
4 thousandths ,, ,, 0·004	,, ,,	1 thousandth ,,	,, 0·001

EXERCISE 5A. *Oral*

Express in words the following numbers:

1. 9·7   **2.** 17·63   **3.** 751·342   **4.** 379·0513
5. 0·37   **6.** 0·048   **7.** 0·0059   **8.** 0·00071
              9. 107·0401   **10.** 786·0031

Express in figures the following numbers:

11. seven and three-tenths
12. nineteen and fifty-four hundredths
13. twenty-five and nine-tenths seven-hundredths
14. three hundred and seven and two-hundredths five-thousandths
15. four hundred and four-hundredths four-ten-thousandths
16. ten thousand and one-tenth one-ten-thousandth
17. three thousand and thirty and one-hundredth seven-hundred-thousandths
18. one hundred thousand and one-hundredth one-hundred-thousandth
19. three million three hundred and three-tenths three-thousandths
20. five million and five and five-hundredths and five-millionths

The fundamental processes of addition, subtraction, multiplication and division may be readily extended beyond the units limit to include tenths, hundredths, etc.

ADDITION

Example 1. Add together 23·406, 45·261, 13·013, 36·547.

```
H. T. U.  t. h. th.
    2  3 · 4  0  6
    4  5 · 2  6  1
    1  3 · 0  1  3
    3  6 · 5  4  7
 1  1  8 · 2  2  7
```

In actual practice the 'H., T., U., t., h., th.' etc. are omitted, but the transition from whole numbers to fractions is clearly indicated by the decimal point.

Note that it is advisable to keep the decimal points in the same vertical line.

Example 2. Add together 17·251, 3·01, 24·3, 7·206.

(A)	17·251	(B)	17·251
	3·010		3·01
	24·300		24·3
	7·206		7·206
	51·767		51·767

To begin with, pupils might find it advisable to fill in '0's' for the missing hundredths, thousandths, etc., as in (A), but thereafter they should move quickly to the lay-out as in (B).

EXERCISE 5B

Add together the following:

1. 4·12, 17·35, 3·57, 12·69
2. 2·507, 34·261, 17·543, 9·645
3. 5·02, 0·014, 31, 1·123
4. 33·03, 365, 4·305, 0·023
5. 56·064, 2·15, 561·2, 43·007
6. 32·601, 310·5, 0·3764, 5·04
7. £3·675, £0·432, £16·81, £0·805
8. 487·12s., 0·414s., 6·9s., 254·001s.
9. 6·606 cwt., 34·5 cwt., 401·05 cwt., 0·067 cwt.
10. 1·015 ml., 0·81 ml., 12·341 ml., 27·6 ml.

Some useful practice in 'horizontal' addition may be obtained by arranging the above questions horizontally and checking the answer obtained by vertical addition.

SUBTRACTION

Example 3. Subtract 28·675 from 31·264.

31·264
28·675
2·589

Example 4. From 20 subtract 17·643.

20·000
17·643
2·357

Note that the whole number 20 may be written 20·000 . . . , the zeroes being repeated as often as is required for the purposes of the question.

5

EXERCISE 5C

1. Subtract 27·64 from 31·71.

2. Subtract 38·751 from 40·604.

3. From 127·683 subtract 120·5.

4. From 321·001 subtract 304·07.

5. From 300 take 297·163.

6. From £129·01 take £117·546.

7. Take 59·705s. from 67·572s.

8. Take 289·6007 tons from 500 tons.

9. Simplify 8·375 + 0·0017 − 0·03415.

10. Simplify 3·275 − 4·001 + 5·314.

11. Simplify 13·234 − 9·65 + 4·82.

12. Add together 0·398, 2·04, 0·003, 10·6 and subtract 1·05 from the sum.

13. From the sum of 12·231 and 6·05 subtract 17·617.

14. From £30 subtract the sum of £13·496 and £12·32.

15. By how much is 17·475 tons less than the sum of 13·201 tons and 6·799 tons?

MULTIPLICATION

When 0·1 $(\frac{1}{10})$ is multiplied by 10, the result is 1

,,   0·3 $(\frac{3}{10})$,,   ,,   ,, 10, ,,   ,,   ,, 3

,,   0·01 $(\frac{1}{100})$,,   ,,   ,, 10, ,,   ,,   ,, 0·1

,,   0·03 $(\frac{3}{100})$,,   ,,   ,, 10, ,,   ,,   ,, 0·3

,,   0·001 $(\frac{1}{1000})$,,   ,,   ,, 10, ,,   ,,   ,, 0·01

,,   0·003 $(\frac{3}{1000})$,,   ,,   ,, 10, ,,   ,,   ,, 0·03, etc.

Thus, in multiplying by 10, thousandths become hundredths,

                        hundredths   ,,   tenths,

                and tenths   ,,   units, etc.

Considering this in relation to the 'decimal point', we might say that when any decimal fraction is multiplied by 10, then the 'decimal point' is moved **one** place to the **right.**

Similarly, in multiplication by 100 the decimal point is moved **two** places to the **right** and in multiplication by 1,000 the decimal point is moved **three** places to the **right** etc.

These rules can be extended to multiplication by several tens and/or hundreds and/or thousands, etc.

By analogy with the foregoing, in multiplication by

    0·1   the decimal point moves **one** place to the **left**
    0·01 ,,   ,,   ,,   ,, **two** places to the **left**
    0·001 ,,   ,,   ,,   ,, **three** places to the **left**

EXERCISE 5D. *Oral*

Multiply the following numbers in turn by 10, 100, 1,000.

    1. 2·35   **2.** 17·356   **3.** 21·02   **4.** 0·346
    5. 2·8467 **6.** 0·01284 **7.** 0·00376 **8.** 0·000597
               9. 2·0037 **10.** 5·00018

Multiply the following numbers in turn by 0·1, 0·01, 0·001.

    11. 1,243   **12.** 345·7   **13.** 23·68   **14.** 1·597
    15. 0·679   **16.** 0·058   **17.** 0·0034 **18.** 70·07
             19. 60·006 **20.** 51·0101

In actual 'long multiplication' two of several methods open to us are illustrated.

Example 5. Multiply 37·42 by 16·34.

(A)   37·42   In this method, whether we start multiplying
       16·34   from the left or right, track is kept of the deci-
      ———   mal point throughout.
      374·2
     224·52
      11·226
       1·4968
     ———
   611·4428

(B)   37·42   In this method, each of the terms being multi-
      16·34   plied together contains hundredths and so the
      ———   product must contain 'hundred-hundredths', i.e.
     14968   ten-thousandths. Hence there must be **four**
     11226   figures after the decimal point. In actual practice,
     22452   we proceed as in ordinary multiplication and then
      3742   insert the decimal point at the end.
     ———
   611·4428

EXERCISE 5E

Multiply:

    1. 31·47 by 23   **2.** 42·58 by 34·2   **3.** 536·9 by 4·53
    4. 6·471 by 0·453   **5.** 7685·2 by 0·015 **6.** 874·9 by 0·0026
    7. 9687·3 by 0·00037 **8.** 0·27 by 0·31   **9.** 0·038 by 0·42
    10. 0·049 by 0·053   **11.** 0·0051 by 0·64 **12.** 0·0062 by 0·075

Find the continued product of:

13. 2, 0·02, 0·002   **14.** 30, 0·3, 0·03   **15.** 1·5, 1·2, 0·09
16. 0·25, 0·04, 50   **17.** 5·3, 0·01, 4·07   **18.** 3·75, 0·8, 1·5
19. 1·43, 0·21, 3·01   **20.** 2·54, 0·032, 5·12

21. Multiply 8·26 by 0·915 and then **write down** the value of 0·826 × 0·0915.

22. Multiply 29·87 by 40·08 and then **write down** the value of 2·987 × 4·008.

23. Multiply 5·023 by 0·47 and then **write down** the value of 0·05023 × 470.

24. Multiply 45·25 by 20·86 and then **write down** the value of 4·525 × 104·3.

25. Multiply 59·86 by 3·408 and then **write down** the value of 0·2993 × 681·6.

DIVISION

It will be useful to consider **division** as a true converse of **multiplication** and reverse the rules accordingly.

When 1   is divided by 10, then the result is 0·1
„ 3   „   „   „ 10, „   „   „   „ 0·3
„   0·1 „   „   „ 10, „   „   „   „ 0·01
„   0·3 „   „   „ 10, „   „   „   „ 0·03
„   0·01 „   „   „ 10, „   „   „   „ 0·001
„   0·03 „   „   „ 10, „   „   „   „ 0·003

Thus, in dividing by 10, units become tenths,
tenths become hundredths,
hundredths become thousandths, etc.

Considering this in relation to the decimal point we say that, when any decimal fraction is divided by 10, then the 'decimal point' is moved **one** place to the **left.**

Similarly, in division by 100, the decimal point is moved **two** places to the **left,** and in division by 1,000, the decimal point is moved **three** places to the **left,** etc.

These rules can readily be extended to division by tens and/or hundreds and/or thousands, etc.

And again, by analogy we may say that in division by

0·1,   the decimal point is moved **one** place to the **right;**
0·01,   „   „   „   „   „   **two** places to the **right;**
0·001, „   „   „   „   „   **three** places to the **right.**

This will be clearer when we realize that division by

0·001, 0·01, 0·1 is equivalent to multiplication by 1,000, 100, 10
1,000, 100, 10   „   „   „   ,   „ 0·001, 0·01, 0·1

EXERCISE 5F. Oral

Divide the following numbers in turn by 10, 100, 1,000:

1. 197653·4   **2.** 28654·2   **3.** 5876·3   **4.** 698·63
5. 80·974   **6.** 9·1083   **7.** 0·476   **8.** 0·0365
                   9. 0·00256   **10.** 0·000143

Divide the following numbers in turn by 0·1, 0·01, 0·001:

11. 0·0000023 **12.** 0·0000341 **13.** 0·000452 **14.** 0·005634
15. 0·067452   **16.** 0·78563   **17.** 8·96745   **18.** 79·8785
                   19. 679·896   **20.** 7,879·432

From a variety of 'long-division' methods we choose that which is probably most widely used and gives rise to fewest errors.
It is the method of making the divisor a **whole** number.

Example 6. Divide 1,015·058 by 21·46.

$$Note. \quad \frac{1015\cdot058}{21\cdot46} = \frac{1015\cdot058 \times 100}{21\cdot46 \times 100} = \frac{101505\cdot8}{2146}$$

$$
\begin{array}{r}
47\cdot3 \\
2146\,)\,\overline{101505\cdot8} \\
8584 \quad\;\; \\
\overline{15665} \\
15022 \\
\overline{6438} \\
6438 \\
\overline{}
\end{array}
$$

$$\therefore \frac{1015\cdot058}{21\cdot46} = 47\cdot3$$

Example 7. Divide 0·93075 by 0·0876

$$\frac{0·93075}{0·0876} = \frac{9307·5}{876}$$

$$\begin{array}{r} 10·625 \\ 876\,)\,\overline{9307·500} \\ 876 \\ \hline 5475 \\ 5256 \\ \hline 2190 \\ 1752 \\ \hline 4380 \\ 4380 \\ \hline \end{array}$$

$$\therefore \frac{0·93075}{0·0876} = 10·625$$

N.B. This method requires the addition of as many zeroes as are required to complete the division, e.g. 9307·5 = 9307·500...

It will be useful now to introduce the method of approximation.

Example 8. Divide 37·621 by 17·63, giving the answer correct to the 3rd decimal place.

$$\frac{37·621}{17·63} = \frac{3762·1}{1763}$$

$$\begin{array}{r} 2·1339 \\ 1763\,)\,\overline{3762·1000} \\ 3526 \\ \hline 2361 \\ 1763 \\ \hline 5980 \\ 5289 \\ \hline 6910 \\ 5289 \\ \hline 16210 \\ 15867 \\ \hline \end{array}$$

$$\therefore \frac{37·621}{17·63} = 2·1339... = 2·134 \text{ (correct to 3rd decimal place)}$$

Rules for approximation to a certain decimal place

1. When the number following that in the required decimal place

is *greater than 4*, then the number should be *increased by 1* in the final decimal place.

2. When the number following that in the required decimal place is 4 or *less than 4*, then the number *remains unaltered* in the final decimal place.

e.g. 15·3562... = 15·356 (correct to 3rd dec. pl.)
27·178... = 27·18 (,, ,, 2nd ,, ,,)
39·48374... = 39·4837 (,, ,, 4th ,, ,,)

EXERCISE 5G

Divide:

1. 17·63 by 4
2. 287·5 by 0·8
3. 3·987 by 0·06
4. 0·4752 by 0·003
5. 0·0582 by 0·012
6. 0·006842 by 0·0011
7. 0·000483 by 0·07
8. 0·01761 by 0·0004
9. 0·2973 by 0·008
10. 0·001876 by 0·00005
11. 241·5 by 2·3
12. 222·005 by 0·35
13. 39·483 by 3·21
14. 236·081 by 0·047
15. 13·1127 by 4·01
16. 0·01491 by 0·035
17. 0·003782 by 0·062
18. 2·36081 by 4·7
19. 810·4704 by 0·0976
20. 4·3046721 by 0·0729

In division of the following numbers answers should be given:
(A) correct to 2nd decimal place.

21. 27·64 by 8·32   22. 387·5 by 94·3   23. 4·985 by 0·076

(B) correct to 3rd decimal place.

24. 16·53 by 7·21   25. 437·61 by 87·6   26. 0·596 by 0·0063

(C) correct to 4th decimal place.

27. 37·48 by 0·67   28. 485·9 by 63·7   29. 0·0689 by 0·43
30. 0·00375 by 0·059

SIGNIFICANT FIGURES

The distance from the Earth to the Sun is normally given as 93,000,000 miles. When we look at this number two questions occur to us. Firstly, are there *no* hundred-thousands, ten-thousands, thousands, etc., in this number? Secondly, is this the distance to the Sun exactly to a mile? To these questions there is one answer, namely, that this is the distance expressed in 'round millions'. In such a case the zeroes in the number are only of interest to us in that they give us the proper order of magnitude of the number, in this

case, millions, but the really **significant figures** are 9 and 3. This becomes clear when we refer to the number as 93 million or 93×10^6 miles, when the significance of the 9 and 3 is obvious. We speak of this 93,000,000 miles as being the distance from the Earth correct to **two** significant figures.

Consider now such a distance as 0·000093 mile correct to a millionth of a mile. Here again we can speak of this distance as 93 millionths of a mile, emphasizing the significance of the 9 and the 3. Once more the zeroes are only important in so far as they indicate the order of magnitude of the number. Hence, 0·000093 mile is also a distance correct to **two** significant figures.

The **significant figures** in any given number, then, are those figures which are left once we have removed any zeroes which precede or follow them.

But we must be careful to distinguish between significant and non-significant zeroes, e.g. in the number 67,000, the significant figures are 6, 7, but in the number 60,007 the significant figures are 6, 0, 0, 0, 7, since the latter definitely states that there are *no* thousands, hundreds or tens.

A **zero,** then, is a significant figure if other numbers precede **and** follow it.

Again, the decimal point does not affect the number of significant figures, e.g. the numbers 6,750, 67·50 and 0·006750 each contain the three significant figures 6, 7 and 5.

There is one exception to which we must draw attention. When a man gives a cheque for £5,000 to charity, then it is understood that this is an exact sum without any additional hundreds, tens or units, in which case 5,000 is a number of **four** significant figures. On the other hand, the total drawings in a Charities' Day collection may be given as £5,000 when it is understood that there are in addition odd hundreds, tens and units. In this case 5,000 is a number of **one** significant figure.

The way in which significant figures are associated with degree of accuracy is illustrated in the following:

In a certain calculation four different pupils are asked to express the same mathematical constant correct to 6, 5, 4, 3 significant figures.

They do so thus:

$$3·14159; \quad 3·1416; \quad 3·142; \quad 3·14$$

and in so doing express this constant in descending order of accuracy.

EXERCISE 5H. *Oral*

State (i) how many significant figures, (ii) what are the significant figures, in each of the following numbers:

1. 57600	**2.** 57060	**3.** 57006
4. 0·0000670	**5.** 0·00607	**6.** 0·60007
7. 43·406	**8.** 4·3046	**9.** 0·0436
10. 200·052	**11.** 2·00052	**12.** 0·0200052
13. 7000·103	**14.** 701·003	**15.** 0·7001003

Express the following numbers to that degree of accuracy in which they will contain 2, 3, 4, 5 significant figures where applicable.

16. 310070·2	**17.** 543·618	**18.** 2·18506
19. 0·035829	**20.** 0·0018608	**21.** 5·205052
22. 201·073	**23.** 0·030158	**24.** 0·001002
	25. 0·000150	

SIMPLIFICATION

Example 9. Simplify $\dfrac{3·823+2·382}{5·51-4·78}$.

$$\frac{3·823+2·382}{5·51-4·78}=\frac{6·205}{0·73}$$
$$=\frac{620·5}{73}$$
$$=8·5$$

Working:
```
      8·5
73 ) 620·5
     584
     365
     365
```

Example 10. Simplify $\dfrac{1·21\times0·08\times0·3}{0·44\times0·12}$.

Multiply numerator and denominator by 100,000.

$$\therefore \frac{1·21\times0·08\times0·3}{0·44\times0·12}=\frac{121\times8\times3}{44\times12\times10}=\frac{11}{20}=0·55$$

Note that by multiplying numerator and denominator by 100,000 we have cleared the expression of decimal fractions and the question has reduced itself to a straightforward simplification of vulgar fractions. The answer, however, is finally expressed in decimal form.

74 A NEW CERTIFICATE ARITHMETIC—I

EXERCISE 5i

Simplify the following expressions completely:

1. $\dfrac{12 \cdot 75 + 2 \cdot 16}{42 \cdot 6}$

2. $\dfrac{2 \cdot 03 \times 1 \cdot 6}{0 \cdot 232}$

3. $\dfrac{0 \cdot 117 \times 3 \cdot 91}{0 \cdot 0207}$

4. $\dfrac{0 \cdot 6 \times 0 \cdot 024}{0 \cdot 8 \times 0 \cdot 09}$

5. $\dfrac{1 \cdot 32 \times 0 \cdot 72 \times 0 \cdot 05}{7 \cdot 5 \times 0 \cdot 0016}$

6. $\dfrac{2 \cdot 6 \times 0 \cdot 08 \times 0 \cdot 06}{0 \cdot 24 \times 0 \cdot 013}$

7. $\dfrac{5 \cdot 1 \times 0 \cdot 3 \times 0 \cdot 004}{34 \times 0 \cdot 02 \times 0 \cdot 0009}$

8. $\dfrac{1 \cdot 64 \times 3 \times 0 \cdot 0078}{1 \cdot 23 \times 0 \cdot 065 \times 0 \cdot 4}$

9. $\dfrac{252 \times 0 \cdot 02}{(0 \cdot 3)^2 \times 700}$

10. $\dfrac{(0 \cdot 3)^2 \times 2 \cdot 5}{4 \cdot 5 \times 0 \cdot 005}$

11. $\dfrac{6 \cdot 42 - 2 \cdot 98 + 14 \cdot 893}{1 \cdot 35 \times 2 \cdot 8}$

12. $\dfrac{14 \cdot 7 \times 2 \cdot 08}{1 \cdot 68} + \dfrac{0 \cdot 162}{0 \cdot 09}$

13. $\dfrac{(2 \cdot 97 + 1 \cdot 035) \times 0 \cdot 64}{2 \cdot 521 - 1 \cdot 72}$

14. $\dfrac{(0 \cdot 2)^3 \times (10 \cdot 2 + 4 \cdot 2)}{(0 \cdot 03)^2 \times (0 \cdot 78 - 0 \cdot 28)}$

15. $\dfrac{\{(1 \cdot 2)^2 - (0 \cdot 1)^2\} \times 0 \cdot 027}{(0 \cdot 87 + 0 \cdot 23) \times (0 \cdot 3)^2}$

16. $\dfrac{0 \cdot 0137 \times 2 \cdot 85}{0 \cdot 429}$ correct to 4th decimal place

17. $\dfrac{15 \cdot 341 \times 7 \cdot 009}{15 \cdot 341 - 12 \cdot 051}$ correct to 4th decimal place

18. $\dfrac{(3 \cdot 37 - 1 \cdot 825) \times 0 \cdot 63}{0 \cdot 0542}$ correct to 3rd decimal place

19. $\dfrac{6 \cdot 07 - (2 \cdot 4 \times 1 \cdot 8)}{(1 \cdot 625 \div 0 \cdot 65) + 4}$ correct to 2nd decimal place

20. $\dfrac{(0 \cdot 623 \times 10) + (5 \cdot 7 \div 10^2)}{(87 \cdot 1 \div 10) - (0 \cdot 0584 \times 10^2)}$ correct to 2nd decimal place

Conversion of VULGAR to DECIMAL Fractions, and vice versa

Example 11. Express $\frac{51}{64}$ as a decimal fraction.

$$64 \begin{cases} 8 & | \ 51 \cdot 000 \\ 8 & | \ \overline{\ 6 \cdot 375000} \\ & \ \overline{\ 0 \cdot 796875} \end{cases}$$

$$\therefore \ \frac{51}{64} = 0 \cdot 796875$$

Example 12. Express $2\frac{37}{53}$ as a decimal fraction correct to the 3rd decimal place.

Consider $\frac{37}{53}$.

$$
\begin{array}{r}
0 \cdot 6981 \\
53 \ \overline{)\ 37 \cdot 000} \\
318 \\
\overline{520} \\
477 \\
\overline{430} \\
424 \\
\overline{60} \\
53 \\
\end{array}
$$

$$\therefore \ 2\frac{37}{53} = 2 \cdot 698 \text{ correct to the 3rd decimal place}$$

Hence, a vulgar fraction may be changed to a decimal fraction simply by the process of division.

Example 13. Express $0 \cdot 8375$ as a vulgar fraction.

$$
\begin{array}{r}
67 \\
335 \\
1675 \\
0 \cdot 8375 = \dfrac{8375}{10000} = \dfrac{8375}{10000} = \dfrac{67}{80} \\
2000 \\
400 \\
80 \\
\end{array}
$$

Certain **vulgar-decimal** fraction relationships should be memorized:

$$\tfrac{1}{10}=0.1; \quad \tfrac{3}{10}=0.3; \quad \tfrac{7}{10}=0.7; \quad \tfrac{9}{10}=0.9$$
$$\tfrac{1}{5}=0.2; \quad \tfrac{2}{5}=0.4; \quad \tfrac{3}{5}=0.6; \quad \tfrac{4}{5}=0.8$$
$$\tfrac{1}{4}=0.25; \quad \tfrac{3}{4}=0.75$$
$$\tfrac{1}{2}=0.5$$
$$\tfrac{1}{8}=0.125; \quad \tfrac{3}{8}=0.375; \quad \tfrac{5}{8}=0.625; \quad \tfrac{7}{8}=0.875$$
$$\tfrac{1}{3}=0.333 \text{ (to 3rd dec. pl.)} \quad \tfrac{2}{3}=0.667 \text{ (to 3rd dec. pl.)}$$
$$\tfrac{1}{6}=0.167 \text{ (to 3rd dec. pl.)} \quad \tfrac{5}{6}=0.833 \text{ (to 3rd dec. pl.)}$$

EXERCISE 5J

Express as decimal fractions:

1. $\tfrac{11}{20}$ 2. $\tfrac{27}{40}$ 3. $\tfrac{43}{50}$ 4. $\tfrac{13}{16}$
5. $\tfrac{23}{32}$ 6. $\tfrac{41}{64}$ 7. $1\tfrac{91}{128}$ 8. $2\tfrac{67}{80}$
9. $3\tfrac{7}{16}$ 10. $2\tfrac{19}{25}$ 11. $5\tfrac{37}{64}$ 12. $4\tfrac{67}{125}$

Express as decimal fractions correct to 3rd decimal place:

13. $\tfrac{7}{9}$ 14. $1\tfrac{11}{12}$ 15. $5\tfrac{17}{21}$ 16. $6\tfrac{19}{24}$

Express as vulgar fractions:

17. 0.84   18. 0.06   19. 0.475
20. 8.0625   21. 16.3675   22. 29.9125
23. 68.0005   24. 89.0405   25. 76.00875

Decimal Fractions of CONCRETE QUANTITIES

Example 14. Find the value of £2.4765+9.84s.+7.56d.

$$£2.4765+9.84s.+7.56d.$$
$$=£2.4765+9.84s.+0.63s.$$
$$=£2.4765+10.47s.$$
$$=£2.4765+£0.5235$$
$$=£3$$

Example 15. Find the value of 0.625 of £2+0.75 of £1 12s.+1.5 of 10s. 2d.−3.25 of 10s.

0.625 of £2+0.75 of £1 12s.+1.5 of 10s. 2d.−3.25 of 10s.
$$=\tfrac{5}{8} \text{ of } £2+\tfrac{3}{4} \text{ of } £1 12s.+1\tfrac{1}{2} \text{ of } 10s. 2d.-3\tfrac{1}{4} \text{ of } 10s.$$
$$=£1 5s.+£1 4s.+15s. 3d.-£1 12s. 6d.$$
$$=£3 4s. 3d.-£1 12s. 6d.$$
$$=£1 11s. 9d.$$

In some questions, as in worked Example 14, it is better to work entirely in decimal fractions.

In other questions, as in worked Example 15, it is better to convert to vulgar fractions.

And in other questions still a combination of both may be useful.

EXERCISE 5K

Find the value of the following:

1. 4·25 of 6s. 6d. −0·22 of 12s. 6d.

2. 2·75 of 3s. 8d. −1·12 of 4s. 2d. +0·125 of 7s. 6d.

3. 5·25 of 18s. +3·5 of 17s. 6d. −8·625 of 16s. 8d.

4. 0·45 of £2 10s. −0·375 of 13s. 4d. −0·07 of £1 5s.

5. 0·375 of £2 +0·75 of £1 12s. +1·25 of 6s. 8d. −3·5 of 10s.

6. 0·25 of £1 +0·125 of 10s. +1·625 of 7s. 6d. −2·5 of 6s. 8d.

7. 1·65 of 5s. 10d. +0·6 of 2s. 11d. −0·375 of 4s. 8d. −0·75 of 1s. 6d.

8. £1·3125 +0·335 of 8s. 4d. −1·6 of 3s. 9d. −0·875 of 2s. 8d.

9. £7·134225 +8·903s. +10·2d.

10. 0·75 guinea +0·375 crown +0·6 of £0·375 −¾ of 2d.

11. 0·25 guinea +0·625 florin +2·125 of 13s. 4d. −0·8 of £1·375

12. 0·5625 ton +0·25 cwt. expressed in cwt. and qr.

13. 0·625 of 1 ton −0·3375 of 10 cwt. +0·125 of 2 qr.

14. 0·0175 ton +3·114 cwt. +0·144 qr.

15. 0·625 of 1 ton −0·3625 of 10 cwt. +0·125 of 2 qr. 8 lb. −1·25 of 8 lb.

PROBLEMS involving Decimal Fractions

Example 16. In every 100 parts by weight, turnips contain 90·47 parts of water. What weight of water is there in a ton of turnips? (Give answer correct to the nearest lb.)

100 lb. of turnips contain 90·47 lb. of water

∴ 1 lb. „ „ „ 0·9047 lb. of water

∴ 1 ton „ „ „ 0·9047 × 2,240 lb. of water

i.e. 2,027 lb. of water

Example 17. A person paid away 0·55 of the contents of his purse and was robbed of 0·3 of the remainder. If in the end he had £3 3s. left, how much had he at first?

$$\text{Let initial sum of money} = £x$$
$$\therefore \text{Amount paid away} = £0·55x$$
$$\therefore \text{Amount left} = £0·45x$$
$$\therefore \text{Amount lost when robbed} = 0·3 \text{ of } £0·45x$$
$$= £0·135x$$
$$\therefore \text{Final amount left} = £(0·45x - 0·135x)$$
$$= £0·315x$$
$$\text{But final amount left} = £3 \ 3s.$$
$$\therefore 0·315x = 3·15$$
$$\therefore x = 10$$

$$\therefore \text{Sum man had to begin with is £10}$$

EXERCISE 5L

1. A piece of gold weighing 1 lb. was made into 50 rings. What was the weight of each, allowing 0·943 oz. waste in manufacturing?

2. The Mint price of gold is £12·49375 per oz. What is the value of a bar of gold weighing 144 lb.?

3. If the cost of making and distributing penny postage stamps averages 0·0845*d.* each what is the gain on the sale of 12 million such stamps?

4. The rails of a railway are 5 yd. at 0° C. and 0·0007605 of their length longer at 65° C. To allow for this increase in length, find, correct to three decimal places of an inch, the least distance between two consecutive rails at 0° C.

5. If 13 be added to half of a certain number, 0·25 of the sum is then 12·625. Find this number.

6. Three persons receive respectively 0·21, 0·16 and 0·13 of a quarter of £25. What remained of the £25?

7. Out of a total force of 48,000 troops, 0·04 of the number were on the sick list and 0·05 of the remainder were non-effective. How many combatants could be mustered?

8. A boy after giving away 0·25 of his pocket money to one companion and 0·875 of the remainder to another, has 1*s.* 6*d.* left. How much had he at first?

9. A man paid 0·15 of a certain sum to one person and 0·62 of the remainder to another. If he then had £48 9*s.*, what had he originally?

10. At an election, the successful candidate polled 0·4 more votes than the other. The number of votes cast was 10,548. How many votes did each candidate receive?

11. A person going on a journey travels 0·3 of the distance on the first day, 0·2 of the remainder on the second, 0·5 of what still remained on the third and the remaining 56 miles on the fourth day. How many miles did he travel altogether?

12. A person gave to A 0·5 of his money, to B 0·5 of what was left, and to C 0·5 of the remainder, and had then 5s. 2½d. left. What had he at first?

13. From a cask of wine 0·25 is drawn off and replaced with water; 0·25 of the mixture is then drawn off and the cask is again filled with water. After this process has been repeated four times altogether, what fraction of the original quantity of wine will be left in the cask?

14. A train starts with its full complement of passengers. At the first station it drops 0·3 of these and takes in 96. At the next it drops 0·5 of the new total and takes in 12. On reaching the third station there are 270 passengers left. What number started?

15. A person settling his bills paid 0·3 of his money to one man, 0·6 of the remainder to another and 0·75 of the rest to a third. If he had £3 3s. remaining, what had he at first?

6

Decimalization of Money and Other Units

The principle of decimalization is comparable to that of reduction, examples of which were given in Chapter 1.

When dealing with the table of money the procedure is as follows:

    (1) to convert pence to shillings, divide by 12,

    (2) to convert shillings to £'s, divide by 20.

Example 1. Express 17*s.* $7\frac{1}{2}d.$ as a decimal fraction of £1.

$$
\begin{aligned}
\text{(A)}\ 7\tfrac{1}{2}d. &= 7{\cdot}5d. \\
&= 0{\cdot}625s. \\
&= £0{\cdot}03125 \\
17s. &= £0{\cdot}85 \\
\therefore\ 17s.\ 7\tfrac{1}{2}d. &= £0{\cdot}88125
\end{aligned}
$$

This can be abbreviated as follows:

$$
\begin{array}{r|ll}
\text{(B)}\ 12 & 7{\cdot}5 & \text{pence} \\
20 & \overline{17{\cdot}625} & \text{shilling} \\
& \overline{0{\cdot}88125} & \text{pound}
\end{array}
$$

$$\therefore\ 17s.\ 7\tfrac{1}{2}d. = £0{\cdot}88125$$

Example 2. Express £3 16*s.* $10\frac{1}{2}d.$ as a decimal fraction of £5.

$$
\begin{array}{r|ll}
12 & 10{\cdot}5 & \text{pence} \\
20 & \overline{16{\cdot}875} & \text{shillings} \\
5 & \overline{3{\cdot}84375} & \text{pound} \\
& \overline{0{\cdot}76875} & \text{of £5}
\end{array}
$$

$$\therefore\ £3\ 16s.\ 10\tfrac{1}{2}d. = 0{\cdot}76875\ \text{of £5}$$

This method may be extended to include all the other tables of weight, length, etc.

Example 3. Express 3 tons 17 cwt. 3 qr. 21 lb. as a decimal fraction of 10 tons.

$$
28\begin{cases} 4 \\ 7 \end{cases}
\begin{array}{l|l}
 & 21 \qquad\qquad \text{lb.} \\ \hline
 & 5{\cdot}25 \\ \hline
4 & 3{\cdot}75 \qquad\quad \text{qr.} \\ \hline
20 & 17{\cdot}9375 \qquad \text{cwt.} \\ \hline
10 & 3{\cdot}896875 \quad \text{tons} \\ \hline
 & 0{\cdot}3896875 \ \text{of 10 tons}
\end{array}
$$

∴ 3 tons 17 cwt. 3 qr. 21 lb. = 0·3896875 of 10 tons

Example 4. Express 2 miles 5 fur. 8 ch. 11 yd. 1 ft. 6 in. as a decimal of 4 miles correct to the 6th decimal place.

$$
22\begin{cases} 2 \\ 11 \end{cases}
\begin{array}{l|l}
3 & 1{\cdot}5 \qquad\qquad \text{ft.} \\ \hline
 & 11{\cdot}5 \qquad\quad\; \text{yd.} \\ \hline
 & 5{\cdot}75 \\ \hline
10 & 8{\cdot}5227273 \quad \text{ch.} \\ \hline
8 & 5{\cdot}8522727 \quad \text{fur.} \\ \hline
4 & 2{\cdot}7315341 \quad \text{ml.} \\ \hline
 & 0{\cdot}6828835 \ \text{of 4 ml.}
\end{array}
$$

∴ 2 miles 5 fur. 8 ch. 11 yd. 1 ft. 6 in. = 0·682884 of 4 miles

EXERCISE 6A

Express:

1. £3 15s. 7½d. as a decimal of £1

2. £4 5s. 10½d. „   „   „ £5

3. £2 12s. 9¾d. „   „   „ £4

4. £8 13s. 1½d. „   „   „ £10

5. £6 11s. 9¼d. as a decimal of £8 correct to 4th decimal place

6. 1 ton 14 cwt. 2 qr. 14 lb. as a decimal of 1 ton

7. 3 tons 5 cwt. 1 qr. 7 lb.   „   „   „ 10 tons

8. 4 cwt. 2 qr. 10 lb. 8 oz.   „   „   „ 1 ton

9. 2 tons 12 cwt. 6 st. 7 lb.   „   „   „ 4 tons

10. 5 tons 13 cwt. 3 qr. 10 lb. as a decimal of 6 tons correct to 4th decimal place

11. 5 days 21 hr. 45 min. as a decimal of 1 week

12. 2 days 20 hr. 15 min. as a decimal of 2 weeks

13. 4 days 13 hr. 24 min. 45 sec. as a decimal of 1 week correct to 6th decimal place

14. 5 yd. 1 ft. 6 in. as a decimal of 4 furlongs

15. 3 ml. 3 fur. 6 ch. 11 yd. as a decimal of 5 miles

6

The converse process of converting simple decimal quantities of one unit to another related unit is illustrated in the following examples.

Example 5. Express £14·1625 in £ *s. d.*

In this question the whole number of £'s remains unaltered throughout.

$$£14·1625$$
$$20$$
$$\overline{3·2500} \text{ shillings}$$
$$12$$
$$\overline{3·00} \quad \text{pence}$$

∴ £14·1625 = £14 3*s.* 3*d.*

Note that in this process we concentrate on the decimal fraction part at each step in the reduction.

Example 6. Express 6·421875 tons in tons, cwt., qr., lb.

$$6·421875 \text{ tons}$$
$$20$$
$$\overline{8·437500} \text{ cwt.}$$
$$4$$
$$\overline{1·7500} \quad \text{qr.}$$
$$28$$
$$\overline{21·00} \quad \text{lb.}$$

∴ 6·421875 tons = 6 tons 8 cwt. 1 qr. 21 lb.

Example 7. Express 15 cwt. 3 qr. 3 lb. 8 oz. as a decimal of 1 ton. Hence find the cost of 15 cwt. 3 qr. 3 lb. 8 oz. of material at £8 per ton.

$$
28\begin{cases} 4 & 3·5 & \text{lb.} \\ 7 & \overline{0·875} \\ 4 & \overline{3·125} & \text{qr.} \\ 20 & \overline{15·78125} & \text{cwt.} \\ & \overline{0·7890625} & \text{ton} \end{cases}
$$

∴ 15 cwt. 3 qr. 3 lb. 8 oz. = 0·7890625 ton

But 1 ton of material costs £8

∴ 0·7890625 ton ,,   ,,   ,,   £6·3125
$$20$$
$$\overline{6·2500} \text{ shillings}$$

∴ Cost of material = £6 6*s.* 3*d.*

EXAMPLE 6B

Express in £ s. d.
1. £4·65625
2. £3·74375
3. £2·096875
4. £9·046875
5. £17·89375
6. £8·715625
7. 1·146875 of £30
8. £6·951875 to nearest $\frac{1}{4}d$.
9. £5·694725 to nearest $\frac{1}{4}d$.

Express in tons., cwt., qr., lb., oz.:
10. 0·1875 ton
11. 0·16875 ton
12. 0·140625 ton
13. 0·4921875 ton
14. 2·8421875 tons
15. 6·726525 tons to nearest lb.
16. Express 0·8375 mile in fur., yd.
17. Express 0·78675 mile in fur., ch., yd., ft. correct to the nearest foot.
18. Express 0·340625 mile in fur., yd., ft., in.
19. Express 12s. $10\frac{1}{2}d$. as a decimal of £1 and hence find the cost of 1,000 articles at 12s. $10\frac{1}{2}d$. each.
20. Express £5 11s. $10\frac{3}{4}d$. as a decimal of £1 correct to seven decimal places. Hence find the value of 1,000 articles at £5 11s. $10\frac{3}{4}d$. each correct to the nearest penny.
21. Decimalize £3 17s. $8\frac{3}{4}d$. correct to six decimal places. Hence, write down the cost of 200 articles at £3 17s. $8\frac{3}{4}d$. each to nearest penny.
22. Reduce £6 17s. $8\frac{1}{2}d$. to a decimal of £1 correct to six decimal places. Hence, find the cost of 500 articles at £6 17s. $8\frac{1}{2}d$. each to nearest penny.
23. Express 9 cwt. 3 qr. 24 lb. 8 oz. as a decimal of 1 ton. Hence, find the cost of 9 cwt. 3 qr. 24 lb. 8 oz. of goods at £3 11s. per ton (to the nearest penny).
24. Express 3 tons 7 cwt. 2 qr. 21 lb. as a decimal of 1 ton. Hence, find, correct to the nearest penny, the cost of 3 tons 7 cwt. 2 qr. 21 lb. of goods at £2 12s. per ton.
25. Express £77 9s. 6d. as a decimal of £1 and 2 tons 11 cwt. 2 qr. as a decimal of 1 ton. Hence, find the cost of 2 tons 11 cwt. 2 qr. of sugar at £77 9s. 6d. per ton

(i) as a decimal of £1 correct to three decimal places;
(ii) in £ s. d. correct to the nearest penny.

7

Decimal Table of Length and Weight

The Continental systems of length and weight are in many ways more convenient than our own British systems, following, as they do, a 'ten' or decimal principle.

LENGTH

The standard of length in this system is the **metre,** and is the distance between two graduation marks on a Platinum (90%)—Iridium (10%) bar at a temperature of 0° C. This bar is kept in the International Bureau of Weights and Measures near Paris.

As we shall see later, a metre is a little more than a yard, and so it is necessary to have other units of length larger and smaller than a metre to meet the requirements of daily life and commerce. These other units are associated with the metre in multiples of ten or of a tenth part. Thus:

$$\begin{aligned}
10 \text{ millimetres (mm.)} &= 1 \text{ centimetre (cm.)} \\
10 \text{ centimetres} &= 1 \text{ decimetre (dm.)} \\
10 \text{ decimetres} &= 1 \textbf{ metre (m.)} \\
10 \textbf{ metres} &= 1 \text{ Dekametre (Dm.)} \\
10 \text{ Dekametres} &= 1 \text{ Hectometre (Hm.)} \\
10 \text{ Hectometres} &= 1 \text{ Kilometre (Km.)}
\end{aligned}$$

For lengths less than a metre, Latin prefixes are used.

For lengths greater than a metre, Greek prefixes are used.

An examination of this table will make it clear that the various units are derived from each other by a simple decimal process.

Example 1. Express 5 Km. 3 Dm. in metres.

$$\begin{aligned}
5 \text{ Km.} &= 5,000 \text{ m.} \\
3 \text{ Dm.} &= \quad\ 30 \text{ m.} \\
\therefore\ 5 \text{ Km. } 3 \text{ Dm.} &= 5,030 \text{ m.}
\end{aligned}$$

Example 2. Express 2 Hm. 1 Dm. 5 dm. in centimetres.

$$2 \text{ Hm.} = 20,000 \text{ cm.}$$
$$1 \text{ Dm} = 1,000 \text{ cm.}$$
$$5 \text{ dm.} = 50 \text{ cm.}$$

$\therefore$ 2 Hm. 1 Dm. 5 dm. = 21,050 cm.

In actual practice the intermediate steps are omitted and the answer is written down.

Example 3. Express 5,634,081 mm. in Km., Hm., Dm....etc.

Repeated division by 10 leads to the result that

5,634,081 mm. = 5 Km. 6 Hm. 3 Dm. 4 m. 8 cm. 1 mm.

Example 4. Express 123,864 cm. in Km. and fractions of a Km.

$$123,864 \text{ cm.} = 1 \cdot 23864 \text{ Km.}$$

For the most part work in the Metric system can be done without lengthy written calculation.

Frequently it is convenient to change from the Metric to the British system, and vice versa, and for this purpose the following facts are useful.

Conversion Table

1 inch = 2·54 cm.   1 cm. = 0·3937 in.

1 m. = 39·37 in.

1 Km. = 1,094 yd. = $\frac{5}{8}$ mile (approx.).

Example 5. Express the speed of 1·2 Km. per minute in miles per hour.

Distance travelled in 1 minute = 1·2 Km. = $1 \cdot 2 \times \frac{5}{8}$ ml.

$$\therefore \quad \text{,,} \quad \text{,,} \quad \text{,, 1 hour} = \frac{\overset{3}{\cancel{6}}}{\underset{1}{\cancel{5}}} \times \frac{\overset{1}{\cancel{5}}}{\underset{4}{\cancel{8}}} \times \overset{15}{\cancel{60}} = 45 \text{ ml.}$$

$\therefore$ Speed = 45 m.p.h.

Exercise 7a

Express:

1. 5,478 mm. in m., dm., cm., mm.

2. 40,671 cm. in Hm., Dm., m., dm., mm.

3. 3,206,904 mm. in Km., Hm., Dm., m., dm., cm., mm.

4. 2,843 m. in Km., Hm., Dm., m.

5. 41,076 dm. in Hm., Dm., m., dm.

Express:

6. 3 dm. 5 mm. in mm.

7. 2 Dm. 4 m. 7 cm. in cm.

8. 1 Km. 3 Dm. 2 m. in dm.

9. 7 Hm. 4 dm. 5 cm. in mm.

10. 3 Km. 6 Hm. 1 m. 7 dm. 8 mm. in mm.

11. By how much is 8 inches more than 20 cm.? (Answer in cm.)

12. Which is the greater and by how much—10 inches *or* 25 cm. (Answer in inches.)

13. By how many inches is the 110 yards race longer than the 100 metres?

14. Which is the longer race and by how much—the 10 Km. *or* 6 mile? (Answer in yards.)

15. If 1 yard=9 dm. 1 cm. 4 mm., which is the larger sprint and by how much—the 110 yards *or* the 100 metres? (Answer in mm.)

16. If 1 Km. = 0·62 miles, which is the longer race and by how much—the 50 Kilometre *or* the 30 mile? (Answer in miles.)

17. How many steps of 85 cm. must be taken in walking a distance of 1 Km. 56 m. 55 cm.?

18. Express the sum of 2 Dm. 4 m. 9 dm.; 7 m. 6 cm.; and 5 Dm. 3 m. 4 dm. 8 cm. in metres, and divide the result by 48.

19. A motor-car is travelling at the rate of 960 metres per minute. Find its speed in miles per hour.

20. Express a speed of 1·6 Km. per minute in miles per hour.

21. Express a speed of $\frac{2}{3}$ miles per minute in metres per sec.

22. Express a speed of 44 ft. per second in Km. per hour.

23. The world's record for the high jump in 1955 was 6 ft. 11$\frac{1}{2}$ in. How much is this greater than 2 metres? (Answer in inches.)

24. An athlete runs 12 ml. 780 yd. in 1 hour. Express this as a rate in metres per second correct to the 1st decimal place.

25. The radius of the earth is 4,000 miles. Express this in Kilometres to the 1st decimal place.

26. The world record for the 100 metres is 10·2 sec. The world record for the 100 yards is 9·3 sec. Find, in inches per second, which is the faster speed.

27. In 1952, Emil Zatopek created a world record of 1 hr. 19 min. 11·8 sec. for the 25 Kilometres, and in 1948, M. Hietanen ran 15 miles in 1 hr. 17 min. 28·6 sec. Which is the faster rate, reckoned in yards per second, and by how much?

28. A certain petrol gives 32 miles to the gallon. How much fuel would be required on the Continent in making a journey of 1,000 Km.? (Answer to nearest gallon.)

29. 1 metre of cloth costs 840 francs. Find the equivalent cost in shillings and pence if 980 francs = £1. (Answer to nearest penny.)

30. Before crossing to France a motorist filled the tank of his car with 8 gallons of petrol at 4s. 4½d. per gallon. This quantity of fuel enabled him to run 448 Kilometres. Find (1) how many miles he travelled per gallon of petrol; (2) the cost per mile of his journey.

WEIGHT

The Continental or Metric Table of Weight is very similar to that of Length. By writing 'gram' for 'metre' in the length table, the table of weight is obtained.

10 milligrams (mg.)	= 1 centigram	(cg.)
10 centigrams	= 1 decigram	(dg.)
10 decigrams	= 1 **gram**	(g.)
10 **grams**	= 1 Dekagram	(Dg.)
10 Dekagrams	= 1 Hectogram	(Hg).
10 Hectograms	= 1 Kilogram	(Kg.)

Conversion Table

1 Kilogram = 2·2 lb.
1 lb.   = 0·45 Kg.

Example 6. Express 5,047 dg. in Kg., etc.

Repeated division by 10, marking off from the units end of the 5,047, gives the result

5,047 dg. = 5 Kg. 4 Dg. 7 g.

Example 7. Express 4 Hg. 3 g. in centigrams.

$$4 \text{ Hg.} = 40{,}000 \text{ cg.}$$
$$3 \text{ g.} = 300 \text{ cg.}$$
$$\therefore 4 \text{ Hg. 3 g.} = 40{,}300 \text{ cg.}$$

Example 8. Which is the heavier and by how much—50 Kg. *or* 1 cwt.?

$$1 \text{ Kg.} = 2 \cdot 2 \text{ lb.}$$
$$\therefore 50 \text{ Kg.} = 110 \text{ lb.}$$
$$1 \text{ cwt.} = 112 \text{ lb.}$$

$$\therefore 1 \text{ cwt. is heavier than } 50 \text{ Kg. by } 2 \text{ lb.}$$

EXERCISE 7B

Express:

1. 4,307 mg.   in g., dg., cg., mg.
2. 1,072 g.   in Kg., Hg., Dg., g.
3. 50,265 dg.   in Hg. Dg., g., dg.
4. 39,053 cg.   in Hg., Dg., g., dg., cg.
5. 4,035,083 mg. in Kg., Hg., Dg., g., dg., cg., mg.

Express:

6. 5 dg. 7 mg.   in mg.
7. 3 Dg. 4 g. 9 cg.   in cg.
8. 2 Kg. 9 Dg. 5 g.   in dg.
9. 9 Hg. 3 dg. 5 cg.   in mg.
10. 8 Kg. 5 Hg. 2 g. 6 dg. 7 mg. in mg.
11. Express in Kilograms the total weight of sugar in 58 bags if each contains 1 Kg. 275 g.
12. Which is the heavier and by how much—a box weighing $2\frac{3}{4}$ cwt. *or* one weighing 140 Kg.? (Answer in lb.; assume 1 lb. $=0 \cdot 45$ Kg.)
13. A bar of metal weighs 12·2 lb. in the British system and 5·5 Kg. in the Metric system. Use this to find the number of lb. in 1 Kg. correct to 1st decimal place.
14. If one penny weighs 0·35 oz. and 1 lb. $=0 \cdot 45$ Kg., what is the weight in grams of a bag containing 8*s*. in pennies?
15. 10 metres of a certain wire weigh 2·75 gm. Find:
 (i) the weight of 100 metres in grams;
(ii) ,,   ,,   ,, 100 yards in grams correct to 3rd decimal place;
(iii) ,,   ,,   ,, 100 yards in ounces correct to 1st decimal place.

8

Area of Rectangle and Square

To find Area of a Rectangle given its Length and Breadth

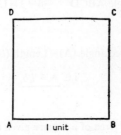

Suppose that on a line AB of length 1 unit a square ABCD is drawn, then the surface enclosed within the boundary lines of the square ABCD is called the **area** of the square.

Area of square ABCD = 1 square unit.

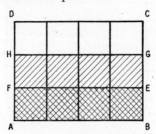

Consider the line AB = 4 units. On each unit of length in AB draw a square.

Then,

area of rectangle ABEF = 4 × 1 = 4 sq. units

On each unit of length in FE draw a square.

Then,

area of rectangle ABGH = 4 × 2 = 8 sq. units

On each unit of length in HG draw a square.
Then,

area of rectangle ABCD = 4 × 3 = 12 sq. units

In the rectangle ABCD,

Length of rectangle ABCD = 4 units
Breadth of rectangle ABCD = 3 units
Area of rectangle ABCD   = 4 × 3 = 12 sq. units

Hence,

Area of any rectangle (A) = Length (l) × Breadth (b)

i.e. $\underline{A = l.b.}$

To find Area of a Square given its Side

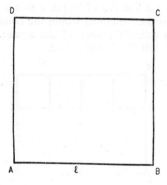

A square is really a rectangle with adjacent sides equal, i.e. $l = b$.

∴ Area of square (A) = length (l) × length (l),

i.e. $\underline{A = l^2}$

This result can be used to establish the table of area.

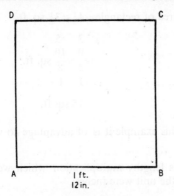

D ⌐ C

A ⌐ B

1 ft.
12 in.

Suppose ABCD represents a square of side 1 ft. or 12 in.

Area of square ABCD = 1 sq. ft.
" " " ABCD = 12^2 sq. in. = 144 sq. in.
∴ 144 sq. in. = 1 sq. ft.
Similarly   9 sq. ft. = 1 sq. yd.
4,840 sq. yd. = 1 acre
640 acres = 1 sq. mile

In farming communities 1 acre is frequently regarded as the area of a square of side 70 yd. Normally these 'yards' are the farmer's paces and altogether a useful approximation is obtained in this way.

Example 1. Find the area of a rectangle 4 ft. 6 in. long and 3 ft. 4 in. broad.

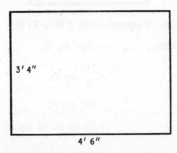

3′ 4″

4′ 6″

Length of rectangle = 4 ft. 6 in. = $4\frac{1}{2}$ ft.
Breadth of rectangle = 3 ft. 4 in. = $3\frac{1}{3}$ ft.

∴ Area of rectangle $=4\frac{1}{2}\times3\frac{1}{3}$ sq. ft.

$$=\frac{\overset{3}{\cancel{9}}}{\underset{1}{\cancel{2}}}\times\frac{\overset{5}{\cancel{10}}}{\underset{1}{\cancel{3}}}\ \text{sq. ft.}$$

$$=15\ \text{sq. ft.}$$

Note that in this example it is of advantage to work in the unit of feet.

This (i) avoids lengthy multiplication which would be required if the unit were inches;

    (ii) avoids lengthy division by 144 to reduce sq. in to sq. ft.

Example 2. Find the area of a square of side 5 ft. 4 in.

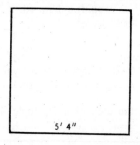

5' 4"

Side of square $=5$ ft. 4 in. $=5\frac{1}{3}$ ft.

∴ Area ,,   ,, $=(5\frac{1}{3})^2$ sq. ft.

$$=\frac{256}{9}\ \text{sq. ft.}$$

$$=28\frac{4}{9}\ \text{sq. ft.}$$

$$=28\ \text{sq. ft. 64 sq. in.}$$

Example 3. Find the cost of a carpet 15 ft. 4 in. long and 12 ft. broad at 27*s.* per square yard.

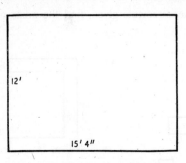

Area of carpet $= 15\frac{1}{3} \times 12$ sq. ft.
$= 184$ sq. ft.
$= 20\frac{4}{9}$ sq. yd.

But 1 sq. yd. of carpet costs 27s.

∴ $20\frac{4}{9}$ sq. yd. of carpet costs $\dfrac{\overset{}{184}}{\underset{1}{9}} \times \overset{3}{27}s.$

$= 552s.$

∴ Cost of carpet $= £27 \ 12s.$

EXERCISE 8A

Find the areas of the following rectangles:

	Length	*Breadth*		*Length*	*Breadth*
1.	8 ft.	1 ft. 3 in.	**2.**	5 ft. 4 in.	3 ft. 6 in.
3.	7 ft. 6 in.	4 ft. 2 in.	**4.**	3 yd. 1 ft.	4 ft. 6 in.
5.	5 yd. 9 in.	3 yd. 1 ft.	**6.**	385 yd.	143 yd.
7.	$1\frac{1}{2}$ ml.	88 yd.	**8.**	0·32 ml.	0·18 ml.

Find the areas of the following squares whose sides are:

9. 1 ft. 4 in.   **10.** 3 ft. 3 in.   **11.** 5 yd. 1 ft.

12. 2 yd. 9 in.   **13.** 0·12 ml.

Using the measurements given, find the areas of the following figures:

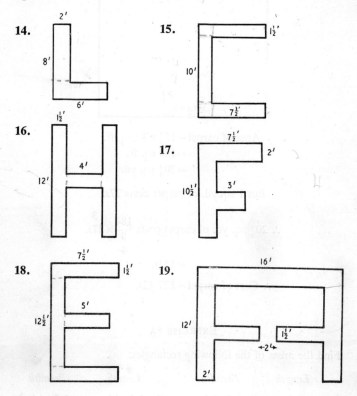

20. Find the area, in acres, of a straight road $5\frac{1}{2}$ miles long and 88 ft. wide.

21. If it cost £16 10s. to lay linoleum on a floor 16 ft. 6 in. by 15 ft., find the price of the linoleum per square yard.

22. Find the cost of fitting a carpet in a square room of side 15 ft. at 36s. per sq. yd.

23. A field is $\frac{1}{4}$ mile long and $\frac{1}{5}$ mile broad. Find the cost of ploughing it at £2 15s. per acre.

24. How many pieces of paper each $\frac{1}{2}$ in. by $\frac{3}{4}$ in. can be cut from a sheet 5 in. by 9 in.?

25. Find the area of a floor 24 ft. long and 16 ft. 6 in. broad. How many tiles, each 9 in. by 4 in., would be required to pave the floor?

26. A metal sheet 5 ft. 4 in. long and 3 ft. 9 in. broad weighs 24 lb. What is the weight of another sheet, $6\frac{1}{4}$ ft. square, made of the same material and of the same thickness as the first?

27. In a row of 12 houses each house has 17 windows, each window 4 panes, and each pane measures 18 in. by 9 in. What will it cost for glass for all the houses, if glass costs 1s. 3d. per sq. ft.?

28. Find the cost of paving a piece of ground, 20 yd. long and 20 ft. wide, with slabs each 1 ft. long and 9 in. wide, costing 5s. per dozen.

29. Find the cost of turfing a rectangular plot of ground 140 ft. long and 80 ft. broad with pieces of turf 3 ft. 6 in. long and 2 ft. broad, at the rate of 18s. 9d. per 100 pieces.

30. Planks 5 in. wide and 4 ft. high are placed side by side to form a paling round a plot of ground 35 yd. long and 25 yd. wide. How many planks would be required and what would they cost if the wood is $4\frac{1}{2}d.$ per sq. ft.?

To find the Length or Breadth of a Rectangle given its Area

We have seen that

$$\text{Area of a rectangle} = \text{Length} \times \text{Breadth}$$

$$\text{i.e. } A = l \times b$$

$$\therefore l = \frac{A}{b}$$

$$\text{and } b = \frac{A}{l}$$

$$\therefore \text{Length of rectangle} = \frac{\text{Area}}{\text{Breadth}}$$

$$\text{and Breadth of rectangle} = \frac{\text{Area}}{\text{Length}}$$

Example 4. It costs £35 12s. 6d. to carpet the floor of a room $14\frac{1}{4}$ ft. wide with carpet at 25s. per square yard. Find the length of the room.

$$£1\tfrac{1}{4}=\text{cost of 1 sq. yd. of carpet}$$

$$\therefore \ £35\tfrac{5}{8}=\text{cost of }\frac{\overset{57}{\cancel{285}}}{\cancel{8}}\times\frac{\overset{1}{\cancel{4}}}{\cancel{5}}\text{ sq. yd. of carpet.}$$
$$\phantom{\therefore \ £35\tfrac{5}{8}=\text{cost of }}\underset{2}{}\ \underset{1}{}$$

$$=\text{cost of }28\tfrac{1}{2}\text{ sq. yd. of carpet.}$$

$$\therefore \ \text{Area of carpet}=28\tfrac{1}{2}\text{ sq. yd.}=28\tfrac{1}{2}\times9\text{ sq. ft.}$$

$$\text{Width of carpet}=14\tfrac{1}{4}\text{ ft.}$$

$$\therefore \ \text{Length of carpet}=\frac{28\tfrac{1}{2}\times9}{14\tfrac{1}{4}}\text{ ft.}$$

$$=\frac{\overset{1}{\cancel{57}}\times9\times\overset{2}{\cancel{4}}}{\underset{1}{\cancel{2}}\times\underset{1}{\cancel{57}}}\text{ ft.}$$

$$\therefore \ \text{Length of room}=18\text{ ft.}$$

EXERCISE 8B

Find the breadth of each of the following rectangles:

	Area	Length		Area	Length
1.	126 sq. ft.	18 ft.	**2.**	14 sq. yd.	$10\tfrac{1}{2}$ ft.
3.	11 sq. yd. 5 sq. ft.	19 ft. 6 in.	**4.**	$\tfrac{1}{2}$ acre	88 yd.

Find the length of each of the following rectangles:

	Area	Breadth
5.	228 sq. ft.	14 ft. 3 in.
6.	17 sq. ft. 72 sq. in.	• 3 ft. 4 in.
7.	57 sq. yd. 7 sq. ft.	5 yd. 1 ft. 3 in.
8.	8 sq. yd. 2 sq. ft. 36 sq. in.	3 yd. 1 ft. $1\tfrac{1}{2}$ in.

In the following questions the length of the side of a square is given and one of the sides of a rectangle of the same area. Find the other side of the rectangle.

	Square	Rectangle
9.	Side = 16 ft.	Length = 21 ft. 4 in.
10.	Side = 12 ft. 6 in.	Breadth = 9 ft. $4\tfrac{1}{2}$ in.
11.	Side = 3 yd. 1 ft.	Length = 8 ft. 4 in.
12.	Side = 5 yd. 9 in.	Breadth = 24 ft. 6 in.

13. Find the cost of flooring a room 18 ft. long and 11 ft. 3 in. broad with planking $4\frac{1}{2}$ in. wide at a cost of 4s. 4d. per linear yard.

14. A stone slab 16 ft. 9 in. long costs £18 8s. 6d. at 6s. per sq. ft. Find the width of the slab.

15. It costs £22 13s. 3d. to carpet a room 18 ft. 6 in. long. If the carpet costs 18s. per sq. yd., find the width of the room.

16. A field 80 yd. long and 50 yd. broad contains 3 red blaes tennis courts each 78 ft. by 36 ft. If the rest of the field is turf, find the cost of turfing at $6\frac{3}{4}d$. per sq. ft.

17. The area of a rectangular garden is 3,630 sq. yd. and its breadth is 55 yd. Find:

      (i) the length of the garden;

      (ii) the cost of fencing it at 2s. 3d. per yd.

18. The area of a rectangular field is 3 acres 224 sq. yd. Its breadth is 76 yd. Find:

      (i) the length of the field;

      (ii) the cost of fencing it at 2s. 6d. per yd.

19. A rectangular field which is 225 yd. long has an area of $5\frac{5}{8}$ acres. Find:

      (i) the breadth of the field;

      (ii) the cost of fencing it at 2s. 9d. per yd.;

      (iii) the cost of cultivation at the rate of £3 13s. 4d. per acre.

20. The area of a rectangular field is 3 acres 4,330 sq. yd. and its length is 145 yd. Find its breadth. How long will a man, walking at $3\frac{3}{4}$ ml. per hr., take to walk round the edge of the field?

Area of Borders

The diagram represents a rectangular room ABCD with a rectangular carpet PQRS laid centrally in the room with a border round about it. Then:

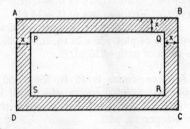

Area of Border = Area of Room − Area of Carpet

Suppose width of border = x units
Then, if length of room = l units
          length of carpet = $(l-2x)$ units
and breadth of room = b units
          breadth of carpet = $(b-2x)$ units
∴ Area of room = $l.b$ sq. units
∴ Area of carpet = $(l-2x)(b-2x)$ sq. units

∴ Area of border = $[lb-(l-2x)(b-2x)]$ sq. units
$= (lb-lb+2lx+2bx-4x^2)$ sq. units
$= 2x(l+b-2x)$ sq. units

This formula should **not** be memorized. Each question should be worked out from first principles using the information given.

Note that when the carpet is placed centrally in the room, then its length and breadth are obtained by subtracting **twice** the width of the border from the length and breadth of the room.

Example 5. A path 3 ft. wide surrounds a garden plot 36 ft. long and 28 ft. broad. Find the area of the path.

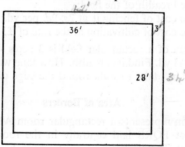

Length of plot + path = $(36+6)$ ft. = 42 ft.
Breadth of plot + path = $(28+6)$ ft. = 34 ft.
∴ Area of plot + path = 42×34 sq. ft. = 1,428 sq. ft.
But area of plot = 36×28 sq. ft. = 1,008 sq. ft.
∴ Area of path = 420 sq. ft.

Example 6. A dining-room is 15 ft. long and 12 ft. broad. What are the dimensions of a carpet which will leave a border 1 ft. 6 in. all round? What is the cost of covering the border with linoleum at 11*s*. 6*d*. per sq. yd.?

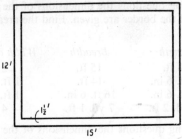

Length of carpet = 12 ft.
Breadth of carpet = 9 ft.
∴ Area of carpet = 12 × 9 sq. ft. = 108 sq. ft.
But area of room = 15 × 12 sq. ft. = 180 sq. ft.
∴ Area of border = 72 sq. ft. = 8 sq. yd.

1 sq. yd. of linoleum costs 11s. 6d.
∴ 8 ,, ,, ,, ,, ,, 92s. = £4 12s.

∴ Cost of covering border with linoleum = £4 12s.

EXERCISE 8C

Find the area of the border in each of the following cases from information given:

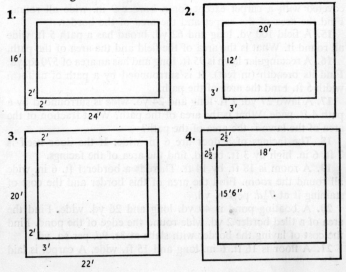

In the following questions the dimensions of the *outer* rectangle and the width of the border are given. Find the area of the border in each case.

	Length	Breadth	Width of Border
5.	18 ft.	15 ft.	2 ft.
6.	17 ft. 6 in.	14 ft.	1 ft. 6 in.
7.	19 ft. 6 in.	16 ft. 6 in.	1 ft. 3 in.
8.	10 yd. 2 ft.	7 yd. 1 ft.	4 ft.

In the following questions the dimensions of the *inner* rectangle and the width of the border are given. Find the area of the border in each case.

	Length	Breadth	Width of Border
9.	20 ft.	17 ft.	1 ft. 6 in.
10.	15 ft. 6 in.	12 ft.	2 ft. 4 in.
11.	17 ft. 6 in.	14 ft. 6 in.	1 ft. 3 in.
12.	8 yd. 1 ft.	6 yd. 2 ft.	4 ft.

13. The floor of a room is 15 ft. by 12 ft. It is covered by a carpet, leaving a border 1 ft. wide all round. Find the area of the border.

14. The floor of a room 22 ft. 6 in. long and 15 ft. 6 in. wide is covered with a carpet except for a border 9 in. wide all round. Find the area of the carpet and the area of the border.

15. A field 100 yd. long and 62 yd. broad has a path 5 ft. wide all round it. What is the area of the field and the area of the path.

16. A rectangular lawn is 95 ft. long and has an area of 570 sq. yd. Find its breadth (in feet). It is surrounded by a path of uniform width 5 ft. Find the area of the path.

17. A lawn 27 yd. 1 ft. long and 24 yd. wide is surrounded by a path 4 ft. wide. What is the area of the path? What fraction of the area of the lawn is the area of the path?

18. The facings of a door are 6 in. wide. If the door itself is 7 ft. 6 in. high by 3 ft. broad, find the area of the facings.

19. A room is 18 ft. by 14 ft. There is a border 1 ft. 6 in. wide all round the room. Find the area of this border and the cost of staining it at $7\frac{1}{2}d.$ per sq. yd.

20. A boating pond is 40 yd. long and 26 yd. wide. Find the area of a tiled border 2 yd. wide round the edge of the pond. Find the cost of laying the border with slabs at 3s. 9d. per sq. yd.

21. A floor is 16 ft. 6 in. long and 15 ft. wide. A carpet is laid

on it, leaving a margin of 15 in. wide all round. Find the cost of covering this margin with linoleum at 7s. 6d. per sq. yd.

22. A carpet 15 ft. 6 in. square is laid in the middle of a room, leaving a border 3 ft. 6 in. wide on two sides and 2 ft. 6 in. wide on the other two sides. Find the area of this border and the cost of covering it with felt at 6s. 9d. per sq. yd.

23. A lawn, 44 ft. long and 24 ft. broad, is surrounded by a gravel path 3 ft. wide. If the cost of turfing is 3s. per sq. yd, and the cost of laying down the gravel is 1s. $1\frac{1}{2}d$. per sq. yd., find the total cost of renewing the lawn and path.

24. Find the cost of turfing a rectangular plot 80 ft. long and 65 ft. wide with pieces 2 ft. 8 in. by 1 ft. 6 in. at £1 2s. 6d. per 100 pieces. If this plot is surrounded by a uniform path 4 ft. wide, find the area of the path and the cost of laying it with ashes at $10\frac{1}{2}d$. per sq. yd.

25. A room is 25 ft. long and 17 ft. broad. What will it cost to carpet it at 36s. per sq. yd., leaving uncovered a margin 3 ft. wide? Find the extra cost of covering the margin with matting at 3s. 9d. per sq. yd.

METRIC TABLE OF AREA

We have seen that the metric table of length is a 'tens' table. From this we can discover that the metric table of area is a 'hundreds' table.

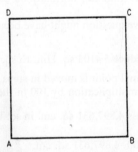

Suppose square ABCD has a side AB of length 1 cm.

Then, area of square ABCD = 1 sq. cm.
But side „ „ „ = 10 mm.
∴ area „ „ „ = 10^2 sq. mm.
= 100 sq. mm.

Thus, 100 sq. mm. = 1 sq. cm.
Similarly 100 sq. cm. = 1 sq. dm.
100 sq. dm. = 1 sq. m.
100 sq. m. = 1 sq. Dm.
100 sq. Dm. = 1 sq. Hm.
100 sq. Hm. = 1 sq. Km.

Conversion Table

1 sq. in. = 6·452 sq. cm.; 1 sq. cm. = 0·155 sq. in.
1 sq. yd. = 0·836 sq. m.; 1 sq. m. = 1·196 sq. yd.

Example 7. Reduce 5 sq. Hm. 41 sq. Dm. 3 sq. m. to sq. m.

(A)   5 sq. Hm. = 50,000 sq. m.
41 sq. Dm. = 4,100 sq. m.

∴ 5 sq. Hm. 41 sq. Dm. 3 sq. m. = 54,103 sq. m.

or   (B) 5 sq. Hm. 41 sq. Dm. 3 sq. m.

100
――
541 sq. Dm.
100
――――
54,103 sq. m.

Reductions of this kind can normally be done without detailed working.

Note that the above question might have been set in the following way:

Reduce 5·4103 sq. Hm. to sq. m.

To do so the decimal point is moved in steps of 2 to the **right** corresponding to each multiplication by 100 in the reduction.

Example 8. Express 4,897,631 sq. cm. in sq. Dm., sq. m., sq. dm., sq. cm.

100	4,897,631 sq. cm.
100	48,976 sq. dm. 31 sq. cm.
100	489 sq. m. 76 sq. dm.
	4 sq. Dm. 89 sq. m.

∴ 4,897,631 sq. cm. = 4 sq. Dm. 89 sq. m. 76 sq. dm. 31 sq. cm.

In actual practice this result would be written as a decimal fraction of the unit of highest denomination.

$$\therefore \ 4,897,631 \text{ sq. cm.} = 4\cdot897631 \text{ sq. Dm.}$$

Example 9. Find the area of a window (correct to the nearest inch) whose length is 15 cm. and breadth is 12 cm.

$$\text{Area of window} = 15 \times 12 \text{ sq. cm.}$$
$$= 180 \text{ sq. cm.}$$
$$\text{But } 1 \text{ sq. cm.} = 0\cdot155 \text{ sq. in.}$$
$$\therefore \ 180 \text{ sq. cm.} = 0\cdot155 \times 180 \text{ sq. in.}$$
$$= 27\cdot9 \text{ sq. in.}$$
$$\therefore \ \text{Area of window} = 28 \text{ sq. in. (app.).}$$

EXERCISE 8D

1. Write in square metres:
     (*a*) 1·235 sq. Km., (*b*) 15634 sq. cm., (*c*) 4835921 sq. mm.
2. Reduce (i) 3 sq. Km. 57 sq. Hm. 17 sq. m. to square metres
     (ii) 37 sq. Hm. 43 sq. Dm. 5 sq. dm. to square centimetres
3. Express (*a*) 72,650 sq. cm. in sq. metres.
     (*b*) 5,136,512 sq. mm. in sq. m., sq. dm., sq. cm.
     (*c*) 107·135 sq. dm. in sq. m., sq. dm., sq. cm.
4. Reduce (i) 54,396,841 sq. mm. to sq. m., sq. dm. etc.
     (ii) 5,189,613 sq. dm. to sq. Hm., sq. Dm. etc.

Find the areas of the following rectangles, giving answers free of decimal points:

Length	Breadth	Length	Breadth
5. 8·4 cm.	7·2 cm.	**6.** 12·5 cm.	1·2 dm.
7. 14·8 m.	8·5 m.	**8.** 325 dm.	2·8 Dm.

Find the areas of the following squares, giving answers free of decimal points:

9. Length of side = 5·6 cm.   **10.** Length of side = 12·4 m.

In the following questions the area and one side of a rectangle are given. Find the other side.

	Area	Length	Breadth
11.	132·3 sq. cm.	12·6 cm.	
12.	30·72 sq. m.		48 dm.
13.	0·4578 sq. Km.		52·5 Dm.
14.	46·488 sq. m.	745 cm.	

15. A booklet is made up of 32 sheets of paper; each sheet is 36 cm. long and 20 cm. wide. Find the area of paper contained in the booklet.

16. What is the greatest number of tickets $6\frac{1}{2}$ cm. long by $3\frac{1}{2}$ cm. broad that can be cut from a sheet of cardboard $1\frac{1}{2}$ metres long and 50 cm. broad? What area of cardboard is left over?

17. How many tiles 20 cm. square will be required to cover the floor of a room 8·4 m. long and 7·5 m. broad? What will they cost at $7\frac{1}{2}d.$ each?

18. A plot of ground 24 m. long and 18 m. broad is surrounded by a path 1·5 m. wide. Find the area of the path.

19. A photograph is mounted so as to leave a plain margin of width 3·2 cm. all round it. If the length and breadth of the photograph are 8·6 cm. by 6·4 cm., find the area of the photograph and hence the area of the mount.

20. A piece of material 24 m. long and 1·2 m. broad is imported from France and sold in this country at 10s. 6d. per sq. yd. Find, to the nearest penny, how much is obtained for the material.

9

Volume of Rectangular Solid

A **Rectangular Solid (or Cuboid)** is a solid each of whose six faces is a **rectangle.** These six faces are made up of three pairs of parallel and equal rectangles.

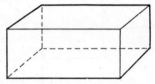

Sometimes this solid is known as a **rectangular prism** and when one pair of opposite faces are squares then it is a **square prism.**

A **Cube** is a special kind of cuboid in which **each face is a square.**

Definition of Cubic Unit

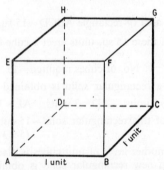

Suppose that on the line AB of length 1 unit a square ABCD is drawn.

Then, area of square ABCD = 1 sq. unit

On square ABCD as base is erected a cube {ABCD; EFGH}.

Then the volume of this cube is that volume enclosed within its six boundary faces

and volume of cube {ABCD; EFGH} = 1 cub. unit

If initial unit of length is the inch, the unit of volume is the cubic inch.

If initial unit of length is the foot, the unit of volume is the cubic foot, etc.

To find the Volume of a Rectangular Solid given its Length, Breadth and Height

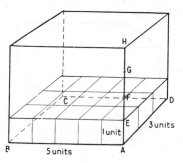

Consider the rectangle ABCD in which AB = 5 units and AD = 3 units.

Then area of rectangle ABCD = 15 sq. units

On each one of these 15 sq. units erect a cube of volume 1 cubic unit

∴ No. of cubes required = 15

By doing this a rectangular solid is obtained having sides

AB = 5 units,   AD = 3 units,   AE = 1 unit

Then volume of this rectangular solid = 15 cubic units

(5 × 3 × 1 cub. units)

Suppose that another layer of unit cubes is placed on top of this first layer; then a new rectangular solid is obtained having sides AB = 5 units, AD = 3 units, AF = 2 units.

And volume of new rectangular solid = 30 cubic units

(5 × 3 × 2 cub. units)

Continuing this process, we find that in the final rectangular solid sides AB=5 units, AD=3 units and AH=4 units.

Volume of given rectangular solid = 5 × 3 × 4 cub. units
                                  = 60 cub. units

Hence, Volume of a rectangular solid (V)
        = Length (l) × Breadth (b) × Height (h)
                i.e. $V = l . b . h.$

To find the Volume of a Rectangular Solid given Area of One Face and Remaining Linear Dimension

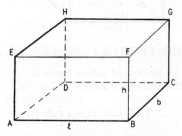

Consider the rectangular solid {ABCD; EFGH} in which

AB = l units, BC = b units and BF = h units

Let area of face ABCD = $A_1 = l.b$ sq. units
   ,,   ,,   ,,   ,,   ABFE = $A_2 = l.h$ sq. units
   ,,   ,,   ,,   ,,   BFGC = $A_3 = b.h$ sq. units

But volume of rectangular solid = $V = l.b.h$ cub. units
                                = $A_1.h$ cub. units
                                = $A_2.b$ cub. units
                                = $A_3.l$ cub. units

To find Volume of a Cube given its Side

A cube is a rectangular solid having all its dimensions (length, breadth, height) equal.

Thus,   volume of cube (V) = length × breadth × height
                           = length × length × length
                           = (length)³

                i.e. $V = l^3$

This result can be used to establish the table of volume.

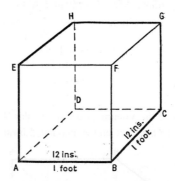

Suppose {ABCD; EFGH} is a cube of side 1 ft. or 12 in.

$$\text{Volume of cube} = 1 \text{ cub. ft.}$$
$$\text{But volume of cube} = 12^3 \text{ cub. in.}$$
$$= 1{,}728 \text{ cub. in.}$$
$$\therefore 1{,}728 \text{ cub. in.} = 1 \text{ cub. ft.}$$

Similarly   27 cub. ft. = 1 cub. yd.

In this work it is frequently useful to be able to change from the table of volume into that of capacity or weight, for which purpose the following couplet is worth memorizing:

> 'A pint of pure water
> Weighs a pound and a quarter.'

Conversion Table

1 cubic foot of water weighs 1,000 oz. or $62\frac{1}{2}$ lb.
1 gallon of water weighs 10 lb.

$$\therefore 1 \text{ cubic foot of water} \equiv 6\frac{1}{4} \text{ gallons}$$

Example 1. Find the volume of the cuboid 7 ft. 6 in. long, 5 ft. 4 in. broad and 3 ft. 3 in. deep.

$$\text{Length of cuboid} = 7 \text{ ft. 6 in.} = 7\frac{1}{2} \text{ ft.}$$
$$\text{Breadth of cuboid} = 5 \text{ ft. 4 in.} = 5\frac{1}{3} \text{ ft.}$$
$$\text{Depth of cuboid} = 3 \text{ ft. 3 in.} = 3\frac{1}{4} \text{ ft.}$$

$\therefore$ Volume of cuboid $= 7\frac{1}{2} \times 5\frac{1}{3} \times 3\frac{1}{4}$ cub. ft.

$$= \frac{\overset{5}{\cancel{15}}}{\underset{1}{\cancel{2}}} \times \frac{\overset{\overset{2}{\cancel{4}}}{\cancel{16}}}{\underset{1}{\cancel{3}}} \times \frac{13}{\underset{1}{\cancel{4}}} \text{ cub. ft.}$$

$$= 130 \text{ cub. ft.}$$

Note that in this example it is a definite advantage to work in the unit of feet.

This (i) avoids lengthy multiplication which would be involved if the unit were inches;

(ii) avoids lengthy division by 1,728 to reduce cubic inches to cubic feet.

Example 2. Find the volume of a cube having side 3 ft. 6 in.

Length of side of cube $= 3$ ft. 6 in. $= 3\frac{1}{2}$ ft.

$\therefore$ Volume of cube $= (3\frac{1}{2})^3$ cub. ft.

$$= \frac{7}{2} \times \frac{7}{2} \times \frac{7}{2} \text{ cub. ft.}$$

$$= \frac{343}{8} \text{ cub. ft.}$$

$$= 42\frac{7}{8} \text{ cub. ft.}$$

$$= 42 \text{ cub. ft. } 1,512 \text{ cub. in.}$$

Example 3. The dimensions of a rectangular tank are 8 ft. 4 in., 2 ft. $7\frac{1}{2}$ in. and 2 yd. 2 ft. Find the weight of water it can hold, giving the answer in lb.

Volume of water in tank $= 8\frac{1}{3} \times 2\frac{5}{8} \times 8$ cub. ft.

But 1 cub. ft. of water weighs 1,000 oz.

$$\therefore \text{ Weight of water in tank} = \frac{25}{3} \times \frac{\overset{7}{\cancel{21}}}{\underset{1}{\cancel{8}}} \times \frac{8}{1} \times \frac{\overset{125}{\cancel{1000}}}{\underset{2}{\cancel{16}}} \text{ lb.}$$

$$= \frac{175 \times 125}{2} \text{ lb.}$$

$$= \frac{21875}{2} \text{ lb.}$$

$$= 10,937\frac{1}{2} \text{ lb.}$$

EXERCISE 9A

Find the volume of each of the following rectangular solids:

	Length	Breadth	Height
1.	6 ft.	5 ft.	4 ft.
2.	4 ft. 6 in.	3 ft. 4 in.	2 ft.
3.	5 ft. 3 in.	4 ft. 8 in.	3 ft. 6 in.
4.	7 yd. 1 ft.	5 yd. 1 ft. 6 in.	10 ft. 6 in.
5.	4 yd. 9 in.	3 yd. 2 ft.	7 ft. 4 in.

Find the volume of each of the following cuboids:

	Area of the Face	Length of remaining Side
6.	39 sq. ft.	3 ft. 4 in.
7.	15 sq. yd.	4 ft. 3 in.
8.	18 sq. ft. 96 sq. in.	4 ft. 6 in.
9.	31 sq. ft. 36 sq. in.	5 ft. 4 in.
10.	17 sq. yd. 4 sq. ft. 72 sq. in.	3 yd. 1 ft.

Find the volume of each of the following cubes with side:

11. 1 ft. 3 in.   **12.** 3 ft. 4 in.   **13.** 5 yd. 2 ft.
14. 4 yd. 1 ft. 6 in.   **15.** 3 yd. 9 in.

16. How many wooden blocks, each 7 in. by 5 in. by 3 in., could be packed in a cellar 14 ft. long, 10 ft. wide and 8 ft. high?

17. How many bricks 9 in. by $4\frac{1}{2}$ in. by 3 in. are required to build a wall 16 ft. long, 6 ft. high and 9 in. thick?

18. Find the cost of digging a trench 20 yd. long, 9 ft. wide and 6 ft. deep at 2s. 4d. per cub. yd.

19. A tank is 5 ft. 4 in. long, 4 ft. 6 in. broad and 3 ft. 3 in. deep. Find the capacity of the tank in gallons if 1 cub. ft. = $6\frac{1}{4}$ gallons.

20. A cubic yard of gravel weighs 30 cwt. and a cartload weighs 1 ton. How many cartloads of gravel can be dug from a hole 10 ft. 6 in. long, 6 ft. wide and 8 ft. deep?

21. A tank is 10 ft. 8 in. long, 4 ft. 8 in. wide and 4 ft. 6 in. deep. If water weighs $62\frac{1}{2}$ lb. per cub. ft., how many tons of water can it hold?

22. An excavator removes $\frac{1}{2}$ cub. yd. of soil and clears it away every 3 minutes. Find the working time to excavate a roadway 20 ft. wide to a depth of 2 ft. 6 in. per 100 yards of length.

23. A swimming pool 22 yd. long and 10 yd. broad is filled to an average depth of $4\frac{1}{2}$ ft. by three pipes in 3 hours. How many

gallons per minute does each pipe supply? (1 cub. ft. of water weighs 1,000 oz.; 1 gallon of water weighs 10 lb.)

24. A camp is supplied with water from a portable tank 8 ft. long, 4 ft. 3 in. broad and 3 ft. 6 in. deep. There are 85 men in the camp and each is allowed $1\frac{3}{4}$ gallons per day. If 1 cub. ft. $= 6\frac{1}{4}$ gallons, find how many days the supply of water in the tank will last.

25. A gravel path 3 ft. wide is made round a grass plot 42 ft. long and 36 ft. wide. Find the area of this path. If it is covered with gravel to a depth of 3 in., find the cost at 22s. 6d. per cub. yd.

Given the Volume of a Rectangular Solid to find the Other Dimensions

We have seen that the volume of a rectangular solid can be written in a variety of ways, depending on which dimensions are given *or* which surface we are considering.

Let dimensions of solid be l, b, h

and   areas of faces of solid be A_1, A_2, A_3

If the volume of the solid $= V$,

then

$$V = l.b.h \quad \ldots \quad \ldots \quad \ldots \quad (1)$$
$$= A_1.h \quad \ldots \quad \ldots \quad \ldots \quad (2)$$
$$= A_2.l \quad \ldots \quad \ldots \quad \ldots \quad (3)$$
$$= A_3.b \quad \ldots \quad \ldots \quad \ldots \quad (4)$$

Hence, given the value of V and certain of the other dimensions, we can find the remaining dimensions.

$$\text{From (1)} \quad l = \frac{V}{bh}; \quad b = \frac{V}{l.h}; \quad h = \frac{V}{l.b}$$

$$\text{,,} \quad (2) \quad h = \frac{V}{A_1}; \quad A_1 = \frac{V}{h}$$

$$\text{,,} \quad (3) \quad l = \frac{V}{A_2}; \quad A_2 = \frac{V}{l}$$

$$\text{,,} \quad (4) \quad b = \frac{V}{A_3}; \quad A_3 = \frac{V}{b}$$

Example 4. The volume of a log of wood 13 ft. 6 in. long is 22 cub. ft. 864 cub. in. Find the area of the end of the log.

$$\text{Volume of log (V)} = 22\frac{1}{2} \text{ cub. ft.}$$
$$\text{Length of log } (l) = 13\frac{1}{2} \text{ ft.}$$

$$\therefore \text{ Area of end of log (A)} = \frac{V}{l}$$

$$= \frac{22\frac{1}{2}}{13\frac{1}{2}} \text{ sq. ft.}$$

$$= \frac{\overset{5}{\cancel{45}}}{\underset{1}{\cancel{2}}} \times \frac{\overset{1}{\cancel{2}}}{\underset{3}{27}} \text{ sq. ft.}$$

$$= 1 \text{ sq. ft. 96 sq. in.}$$

Example 5. The volume of a rectangular solid is 22 cub. ft. If its length is 4 ft. 6 in. and its height 1 ft. 10 in., find its breadth.

    (A) Volume of rectangular solid (V) = 22 cub. ft.
         Length of rectangular solid (*l*) = $4\frac{1}{2}$ ft.
         Height of rectangular solid (*h*) = $1\frac{5}{6}$ ft.

$$\therefore \text{ Breadth of rectangular solid } (b) = \frac{V}{l.h}$$

$$= \frac{22}{4\frac{1}{2} \times 1\frac{5}{6}} \text{ ft.}$$

$$= \frac{\overset{2}{\cancel{22}} \times 2 \times \overset{2}{\cancel{6}}}{\underset{3}{\cancel{9}} \times \underset{1}{\cancel{11}}} \text{ ft.}$$

$$= 2\frac{2}{3} \text{ ft.}$$

$$= 2 \text{ ft. 8 in.}$$

or   (B) Volume of rectangular solid (V) = 22 cub. ft.
     Area of one face of rectangular solid (A) = $4\frac{1}{2} \times 1\frac{5}{6}$ sq. ft.

$$\therefore \text{ Breadth of rectangular solid } (b) = \frac{V}{A}$$

$$= \frac{22}{4\frac{1}{2} \times 1\frac{5}{6}} \text{ ft.}$$

$$= \frac{\overset{2}{\cancel{22}} \times 2 \times \overset{2}{\cancel{6}}}{\underset{3}{\cancel{9}} \times \underset{1}{\cancel{11}}} \text{ ft.}$$

$$= 2\frac{2}{3} \text{ ft.}$$

$$= 2 \text{ ft. 8 in.}$$

Example 6. Water runs into a tank 60 ft. long and 30 ft. wide at the rate of $2\frac{1}{2}$ gallons per second. Find the rate at which the water level rises in inches per hour (1 cub. ft. = $6\frac{1}{4}$ gallons).

Volume of water entering tank per second = $2\frac{1}{2}$ gallons

$\therefore$ Volume of water entering tank per hour (V) = $2\frac{1}{2} \times 3,600$ gallons

$$= \frac{2\frac{1}{2} \times 3600}{6\frac{1}{4}} \text{ cub. ft.}$$

Area of base of tank (A) = 60×30 sq. ft.

$\therefore$ In 1 hr. depth of water in tank $= \dfrac{V}{A} = \dfrac{5 \times 3600 \times 4}{2 \times 25 \times 60 \times 30}$ ft.

$$= \frac{4}{5} \text{ ft.}$$

$$= 9\frac{3}{5} \text{ in.}$$

$\therefore$ Assuming that the water runs in at uniform rate, then the water level will rise at the rate of $9\frac{3}{5}$ inches per hour.

EXERCISE 9B

In each of the following rectangular solids the volume and one dimension are given. Find the area of the appropriate face.

1. Volume = 480 cub. in.   Depth = $7\frac{1}{2}$ in.
2. Volume = 2 cub. yd. 6 cub. ft.   Breadth = 4 ft.
3. Volume = 2 cub. yd. 18 cub. ft.   Length = 1 yd. 1 ft.
4. Volume = 6 cub. yd. 6 cub. ft.   Depth = 3 ft. 6 in.
5. Volume = 5 cub. yd. 15 cub. ft.   Length = 3 yd. 1 ft.

In each of the following rectangular solids the volume and two dimensions are given. Find the remaining dimension.

	Volume	*Length*	*Breadth*	*Height*
6.	70 cub. ft.	4 ft. 8 in.		4 ft. 6 in.
7.	3 cub. ft. 432 cub. in.	2 ft. 3 in.	1 ft. 1 in.	
8.	227 cub. yd. $13\frac{1}{2}$ cub. ft.		15 ft.	10 ft. 6 in.
9.	9 cub. ft. 1,080 cub. in.	2 ft. 9 in.		1 ft. 6 in.
10.	61 cub. yd. 6 cub. ft. 1,296 cub. in.	5 yd. 2 ft. 6 in.	4 yd. 2 ft.	

8

11. A rectangular cistern 2 ft. 6 in. deep contains 4,200 cub. ft. of water. Find the area of its base.

12. There are 3,200 cub. ft. of air in a room 18 ft. long and 8 ft. 4 in. high. What is the width of the room?

13. By drawing off 2,762½ cub. ft. the water level in a storage tank 19 ft. 6 in. wide falls 2 ft. 6 in. What is the length of the tank?

14. The cubic capacity of a room is 1,536 cub. ft. If the height of the room is 12 ft., find the cost of carpeting it at 15s. 9d. per sq. yd.

15. A cube of stone whose edge is 1 ft. 6 in. is totally immersed in a cistern half-full of water. How much will the surface of the water be raised thereby, if the cistern is 6 ft. 8 in. long by 4 ft. 6 in. broad?

16. A cistern 6 ft. 6 in. long, 4 ft. 3 in. wide and 2 ft. 6 in. deep is full of water. If the water is run off into a tank 9 ft. long and 7 ft. 1 in. wide, to what height will the water rise?

17. A tank is 5 ft. long, 4 ft. 6 in. broad and 4 ft. high. How many cubic feet of water can the tank hold? If 70 cub. ft. of water are run into the empty tank, how far from the top of the tank will the surface of the water be?

18. A rectangular tank measuring 11 ft. 6 in. by 10 ft. by 6 ft. 9 in. is full of water. If its contents are run into an empty rectangular tank 15 ft. long and 12 ft. broad, find the depth of water in the latter tank.

19. A metal sheet 8 in. long, 6 in. wide weighs 9 lb. 6 oz. If 1 cub. ft. of the metal weighs 450 lb., find the thickness of the sheet.

20. A tank 16 ft. long and 7 ft. broad contains 12½ tons of water. Find the depth of the water if 1 cub. ft. weighs 1,000 oz.

21. A tank 35 ft. long, 16 ft. wide and 12 ft. deep is filled with water by a pipe which delivers 1,050 gallons per minute.

Find (i) how many inches the water rises per minute;

(ii) the time taken to fill the tank (1 cub. ft. = 6·25 gallons).

22. What must be the depth of a cistern 10 ft. long and 6 ft. 8 in. wide which will contain 2,500 gallons, if a cubic foot of water is equivalent to 6¼ gallons?

23. A rectangular swimming-pool is 30 yd. long and 10 yd. wide and the average depth of the water is 5 ft. 6 in. If 75 gallons of water be drained from the pool per second, find the time which will elapse before the pool is empty (1 cub. ft. = 6¼ gallons).

24. A coal cellar is 5 ft. long, 3 ft. 4 in. broad and 9 ft. high. Find its volume and estimate the number of tons of coal it could hold, assuming that 1 ton of loose coal occupies 60 cub. ft. If

30 cwt. of coal were delivered, calculate the average depth of coal in the cellar.

25. A reservoir of length 350 yd. and breadth 150 yd. has to supply a million gallons of water per day. It contains 27 days' supply. Find in feet the average depth of the water in the reservoir. (1 cub. ft. $=6\frac{1}{4}$ gallons.)

Metric Table of Volume

The metric table of length is a 'tens' table;

,,   ,,   ,, ,, area is a 'hundreds' table;

and now the   ,,   ,, ,, volume is a 'thousands' table.

Thus,

1,000 cubic millimetres (c.mm.)	=1 cubic centimetre (c.cm.)
1,000 cubic centimetres	=1 cubic decimetre (c.dm.)
1,000 cubic decimetres	=1 cubic metre (c.m.)
1,000 cubic metres	=1 cubic Dekametre (c.Dm.)
1,000 cubic Dekametres	=1 cubic Hectometre (c.Hm.)
1,000 cubic Hectometres	=1 cubic Kilometre (c.Km.)

Just as in the British system we are seldom concerned with anything beyond the cubic yard, so in the Metric system the upper limit is normally the cubic metre.

In the British table of capacity, the pint has come to be recognized as the standard; in the Metric table of capacity, the cubic decimetre is the standard, and to it is given the special name of **litre**.

i.e. 1,000 c.cm. $=1$ c.dm. $=1$ **litre**

and thereafter moving downwards we speak of the deci-, centi- and milli-**litre**, and moving upwards we speak of the Deka-, Hecto- and Kilo-**litre**.

Notice that   1 millilitre $=1$ cubic centimetre

and   1 Kilolitre $=1$ cubic metre

It will be useful to remember the following two facts:

1 litre $=0.22$ gallon (approx.)

$\therefore$ 1 gallon $=4\frac{1}{2}$ litres (approx.)

EXERCISE 9C

Express in litres and decimals of a litre:

    1. 5 c.dm., 478 c.cm., 43 c.mm.
    2. 2 c.m., 169 c.dm., 384 c.cm.
    3. 5 D.litres, 8 litres, 4 d.litres, 7 c.litres
    4. 9 H.litres, 3 litres, 5 c.litres, 2 m.litres
    5. 7 Kl., 4 Dl., 3 dl., 4 ml.

Express in Kl., Hl., Dl., l., dl., cl., ml. where relevant:

    6. 5,968,431 c.mm.
    7. 4,857,302 ml.
    8. 3,746·219 cl.
    9. 316·589 litres.
    10. 3 c.m., 17 c.dm., 209 c.cm.

11. Express in cubic centimetres the difference in volume between a cube of side 10 in. and one of side 25 cm. (1 inch = 2·54 cm.)

12. Express to the nearest cubic inch the difference in volume between a cube of side 1 metre and one of side 1 yd. (1 metre = 39·37 in.)

13. Express in pints the difference between the capacity of a 10-gallon milk can and a 50-litre one (1 litre = 0·22 gal.)

14. Assuming that 1 cub. yd. = 0·765 c.m., prove that the nearest whole number of litres in a cubic foot is 28.

15. Assuming that 1 cub. m. = 1·308 cub. yd., prove that 7 cub. metres of water weigh approximately 6·9 tons. (1 cub. ft. of water weighs 62·5 lb.)

16. A river is 26·25 m. wide, 3·44 m. deep and runs at the rate of 3·2 Km. per hour; prove that 4,816 Kilolitres pass a given point per minute.

17. What is the height of a wall which contains 140·625 c.m. and is 90 m. long and 0·3125 m. thick?

18. Find the depth of a tank 43·2 dm. long, 22·5 dm. wide which contains 24·3 cub. metres.

19. The weight of liquid in a cistern, 2·5 dm. long, 2 dm. wide and 1·3 dm. deep, is 3·9 lb. Find the weight of a gallon of this liquid. (1 litre = 0·22 gal.)

20. A rectangular cistern 10 in. long, 8 in. wide and 5 in. deep is full of water. It is emptied into another cistern 3 dm. long and 17·2 cm. broad. What is the depth of water in this second cistern to nearest centimetre? (1 inch = 2·54 cm.)

10

Square Root

When a number is multiplied by itself, then the product is called the **square** of the number.

For example

$16 = 4 \times 4 = 4^2$, so that 16 is the **square** of 4

Conversely, any number is the **square root** of its **square**.
Hence,

4 is the **square root** of 16

The square root of a number is indicated by the symbol '$\sqrt{}$', so that

$$\sqrt{16} = 4$$

In finding the square root of any number (say 'x'), it will be found useful to ask the question, 'What number multiplied by itself gives x?'

In this way the following square roots can be found and should be memorized.

Number	Square Root	Number	Square Root	Number	Square Root
1	1	100	10	361	19
4	2	121	11	400	20
9	3	144	12	441	21
16	4	169	13	484	22
25	5	196	14	529	23
36	6	225	15	576	24
49	7	256	16	625	25
64	8	289	17		
81	9	324	18		

Square Root by the Method of Factors

When the prime factors of a number can be written down, then it is frequently possible to state its square root by inspection.

Example 1. Find the square root of 1,764.

$$
\begin{array}{c|l}
2 & 1764 \\ \hline
2 & 882 \\ \hline
3 & 441* \\ \hline
3 & 147 \\ \hline
7 & 49 \\ \hline
7 & 7 \\ \hline
& 1
\end{array}
$$

$$\therefore\ 1{,}764 = 2^2 . 3^2 . 7^2$$

$$\therefore\ \sqrt{1{,}764} = 2.3.7 = 42$$

*In this example it is obvious that at the '441' stage in the question use can be made of the memorized table which gives $\sqrt{441} = 21$.
Thus,

$$\sqrt{1{,}764} = 2\sqrt{441} = 42$$

EXERCISE 10A

Using the method of factors, find the square root of each of the following numbers:

1. 1,296	**2.** 2,916	**3.** 3,969
4. 5,184	**5.** 9,216	**6.** 11,025
7. 12,544	**8.** 15,876	**9.** 53,361
10. 164,025	**11.** 245,025	**12.** 531,441
13. 1,334,025	**14.** 2,286,144	**15.** 17,935,225

By comparing each of the numbers in the above exercise and the numbers in the preceding list (p. 117). with their corresponding square root, an interesting result is obtained.

No. of digits in number	No. of digits in square root
1	1
2	1
3	2
4	2
5	3
6	3
7	4
8	4

This suggests an easy way of determining the number of digits in the square root of any number.

Consider the number

4435236

Mark off the digits **in pairs,** beginning with the units digit. Thus

4͵43͵52͵36

i.e. in this number there are **four** sections containing two, or, in the final section, one number.

∴ There are **four** digits in $\sqrt{4435236}$ *or* 1 digit per section

Exercise 10b. *Oral*

Write down the number of digits in the square root of each of the following numbers:

1. 729	**2.** 1024	**3.** 2061	**4.** 12769
5. 94249	**6.** 133956	**7.** 383161	**8.** 4435236
	9. 17740944	**10.** 225030001	

Square Root. *General Method*

Example 2. Find the square root of 5846724.

(A)	(B)	(C)
2	5͵84͵67͵24	2418
2	4	
44	184	
4	176	
481	867	
1	481	
4828	38624	
	38624	

We will explain the method in this example in a series of steps.

1. Mark off the digits in pairs beginning with the units digit.

Since number of sections is 4, ∴ there are 4 digits in the square root.

2. Consider the first section, i.e. the number '5'.

What number multiplied by itself produces the highest square less than '5'?

Since the nearest square is 4 and $\sqrt{4}=2$, then the required number $=2$.

3. Place '2' in part A (divisor section) and '2' in part C (quotient section).

Multiply this divisor by quotient and insert result '4' below the '5'.

To the divisor '2' add '2', giving new trial divisor '4', and subtract '4' from '5', giving '1' in part B (dividend section).

4. In part B, bring down the next section '84', making new dividend '184'. Consider the result of dividing '18' by trial divisor '4', leading to the complete divisor 44 since '184' divided by '44' gives '4', which is now inserted in part C (quotient section). At the same time add '4' to '44' to give new trial divisor '48'.

5. Continue this process until complete square root is obtained.

Example 3. Find the square root of 282475249.

```
  1     | 2‚82‚47‚52‚49 | 16807
  1     | 1             ‾‾‾‾‾‾
 ‾‾‾    |
 26     | 182
  6     | 156
 ‾‾‾    | ‾‾‾‾
328     | 2647
  8     | 2624
‾‾‾‾‾   | ‾‾‾‾
33607   |    235249
        |    235249
        |    ‾‾‾‾‾‾
```

$$\therefore \sqrt{282475249}=16,807$$

EXERCISE 10C

Find the square root of each of the following numbers:

1. 529	**2.** 841	**3.** 1156
4. 4761	**5.** 7569	**6.** 9409
7. 16129	**8.** 49284	**9.** 148996
10. 649636	**11.** 5764801	**12.** 5774409
13. 21224449	**14.** 28249225	**15.** 5846743296

Square Root of Decimal Fractions

Example 4. Find the square root of 382·5936.

The number 382·5936 consists of two parts:

      (i) a whole number   382
      (ii) a decimal fraction   ·5936

Essentially the process of finding the square root is as has been described once the number has been 'sectioned' in the following way: $3\,82 \cdot 59\,36$

Starting at the decimal point:

    (1) mark off the whole number in 'pairs' as far as possible.

    (2) mark off the decimal fraction in 'pairs'.

Hence if $\sqrt{382 \cdot 5936}$ is a 'perfect' square root, then that square root is a number consisting of:

    (a) **Two** digits in the whole number part

and (b) **Two** digits in the decimal part.

1	$3\,82 \cdot 59\,36$	19·56
1	1	
29	282	
9	261	
385	2159	
5	1925	
3906	23436	
	23436	

$$\therefore \quad \sqrt{382 \cdot 5936} = 19 \cdot 56$$

Notes (i) It is important that the decimal point be inserted in 'quotient' section immediately the whole number part has been dealt with.

    (ii) When the 'sections' in the decimal part are incomplete then 'zeroes' may be added to complete them.

Example 5. Find the square root of 578·771 correct to 3 decimal places.

2	$5\,78 \cdot 77\,10\,00\,00$	24·0576
2	4	
44	178	
4	176	
4805	27710	
5	24025	
48107	368500	
7	336749	
48114	3175100	

$$\therefore \quad \sqrt{578 \cdot 771} = 24 \cdot 058$$

Example 6. Find the square root of 13 correct to 3 decimal places.

3	13·00	3·6055
3	9	
66	400	
6	396	
7205	40000	
5	36025	
7210	397500	

$$\therefore \ \sqrt{13} = 3{\cdot}606$$

EXERCISE 10D

Find the square root of each of the following numbers:

1. 397404·16
2. 14232·49
3. 3831·61
4. 170·3025
5. 321·4849
6. 5788·1664
7. 6102·7344
8. 40·691641
9. 22·146436
10. 1·83087961
11. 0·13727025
12. 0·01522756
13. 0·07070281
14. 0·00844561
15. 0·0000942841

Find the square root of each of the following numbers correct to 3 decimal places:

16. 43·27
17. 154·39
18. 365·4712
19. 582·361
20. 29·3
21. 4·61
22. 0·572
23. 0·0683
24. 0·00751
25. 7
26. 11
27. 15
28. 0·6
29. 0·07
30. 0·011

The following square roots should be checked and **memorized**:

$$\sqrt{2} = 1{\cdot}414$$
$$\sqrt{3} = 1{\cdot}732$$
$$\sqrt{5} = 2{\cdot}236$$
$$\sqrt{6} = 2{\cdot}449$$

Square Root of Vulgar Fractions

In dealing with the square root of a vulgar fraction a variety of methods should be considered. These are illustrated in the following examples.

Example 7. Find the square root of $6\frac{1}{4}$.

$$\sqrt{6\tfrac{1}{4}} = \sqrt{\frac{25}{4}} = \frac{\sqrt{25}}{\sqrt{4}} = \frac{5}{2} = 2\tfrac{1}{2}$$

Example 8. Find the square root of $5\frac{1}{9}$.

(A) $\sqrt{5\tfrac{1}{9}} = \sqrt{\dfrac{46}{9}} = \dfrac{\sqrt{46}}{\sqrt{9}} = \dfrac{\sqrt{46}}{3}$

$$= \frac{6 \cdot 782}{3}$$

$$= 2 \cdot 261$$

The above method is applicable provided that the denominator of the vulgar fraction is a perfect square.

An alternative method is now suggested.

(B) $\sqrt{5\tfrac{1}{9}} = \sqrt{5 \cdot 111 \ldots}$

$\qquad = 2 \cdot 261$

2	5·11,11,11	2·2607
2	4	
42	111	
2	84	
446	2711	
6	2676	
45207	351111	

Example 9. Find the square root of $3\frac{2}{3}$.

$\sqrt{3\tfrac{2}{3}} = \sqrt{\dfrac{11}{3}}$

$\qquad = \sqrt{\dfrac{11 \times 3}{3 \times 3}}$

$\qquad = \dfrac{\sqrt{33}}{3}$

$\qquad = \dfrac{5 \cdot 745}{3}$

$\qquad = 1 \cdot 915$

5	33·00	5·7445
5	25	
107	800	
7	749	
1144	5100	
4	4576	
11484	52400	
4	45936	
114885	646400	

The method of 8(B) could also be conveniently used.

Exercise 10e

Find the square root of each of the following vulgar fractions:

1. $1\frac{9}{16}$ 2. $2\frac{14}{25}$ 3. $4\frac{25}{36}$

4. $28\frac{4}{9}$ 5. $65\frac{64}{81}$ 6. $5\frac{1}{4}$

7. $3\frac{2}{9}$ 8. $5\frac{13}{16}$ 9. $7\frac{11}{25}$

10. $10\frac{17}{36}$ 11. $3\frac{1}{2}$ 12. $7\frac{2}{3}$

13. $8\frac{4}{5}$ 14. $11\frac{5}{6}$ 15. $24\frac{7}{8}$

Use of Square Root Tables

It is important to understand how the square roots of a variety of numbers may be derived from a square root that is known. For example, starting with $\sqrt{16}=4$ we may deduce that

$$\sqrt{1,600}=40; \quad \sqrt{160,000}=400, \text{ etc.}$$

$$\sqrt{0.16}=0.4; \quad \sqrt{0.0016}=0.04, \text{ etc.}$$

The same, of course, is true when we are dealing with other numbers which are not perfect squares. Hence, starting with $\sqrt{2}=1.414$ we know that

$$\sqrt{200}=14.14; \quad \sqrt{20,000}=141.4, \text{ etc.}$$

$$\sqrt{0.02}=0.1414; \quad \sqrt{0.0002}=0.01414, \text{ etc.}$$

Let us examine this latter example more closely to understand why this is so, i.e. given $\sqrt{2}=1.414$, find (A) $\sqrt{200}$ and (B) $\sqrt{0.0002}$.

(A) $\sqrt{200}=\sqrt{100.2}=\sqrt{10^2.2}=\sqrt{10^2}.\sqrt{2}=10\sqrt{2}$
$$=14.14$$

(B) $\sqrt{0.0002}=\sqrt{\dfrac{2}{10000}}=\sqrt{\dfrac{2}{10^4}}=\dfrac{\sqrt{2}}{\sqrt{10^4}}=\dfrac{\sqrt{2}}{10^2}$
$$=0.01414$$

Original Number	New Number	Original Square Root	New Square Root
25	0.0025	5	0.05
81	810,000	9	900
2	0.000002	1.414	0.001414
3	300	1.732	17.32
5	0.05	2.236	0.2236
6	6,000,000	2.449	2,449

From these we may suggest the rule that:

When any number is multiplied or divided by a multiple of 100 (i.e. 100; 10,000; 1,000,000, etc.), then the square root of the new number so formed is the square root of the original number multiplied or divided by the corresponding multiple of 10 (i.e. 10; 100; 1,000, etc.).

Note, however, that given $\sqrt{2}$ we *cannot* write down $\sqrt{20}$ since the new number 20 is *not* the original number 2 multiplied or divided by a multiple of 100.

From all this we might infer that, given a table of square roots of numbers from 1 to 100 (see pp. 128–31), we will be able to find the square roots of many numbers outwith this range. But first let us learn to read such a table.

SQUARE ROOTS

	0	1	2	3	4	5	6	7	8	9	Mean Differences		
											1 2 3	4 5 6	7 8 9
5·5	2·345	2·347	2·349	2·352	2·354	2·356	2·358	2·360	2·362	2·364	0 0 1	1 1 1	1 2 2
5·6	2·366	2·369	2·371	2·373	2·375	2·377	2·379	2·381	2·383	2·385	0 0 1	1 1 1	1 2 2
5·7	2·387	2·390	2·392	2·394	2·396	2·398	2·400	2·402	2·404	2·406	0 0 1	1 1 1	1 2 2
5·8	2·408	2·410	2·412	2·415	2·417	2·419	2·421	2·423	2·425	2·427	0 0 1	1 1 1	1 2 2
5·9	2·429	2·431	2·433	2·435	2·437	2·439	2·441	2·443	2·445	2·447	0 0 1	1 1 1	1 2 2
6·0	2·449	2·452	2·454	2·456	2·458	2·460	2·462	2·464	2·466	2·468	0 0 1	1 1 1	1 2 2
6·1	2·470	2·472	2·474	2·476	2·478	2·480	2·482	2·484	2·486	2·488	0 0 1	1 1 1	1 2 2
6·2	2·490	2·492	2·494	2·496	2·498	2·500	2·502	2·504	2·506	2·508	0 0 1	1 1 1	1 2 2
6·3	2·510	2·512	2·514	2·516	2·518	2·520	2·522	2·524	2·526	2·528	0 0 1	1 1 1	1 2 2
6·4	2·530	2·532	2·534	2·536	2·538	2·540	2·542	2·544	2·546	2·548	0 0 1	1 1 1	1 2 2

The above table gives the square roots of numbers between 5·5 and 6·499 inclusive.

1. The first column gives the numbers between 5·5 and 6·4 inclusive at intervals of 0·1.

2. The second column (under the number '0') gives the square roots of these numbers 5·50, 5·60, ... 6·40.

3. The following nine columns (numbered '1' to '9') give the square roots of many different numbers. In particular, the first row gives the square roots of the numbers 5·51, 5·52, ... 5·59. Note that these columns numbered '0' to '9' enable us to find the square roots of certain numbers of two decimal places.

4. The 'mean differences' columns (numbered '1' to '9') take us a step further and supply us with those numbers which must be *added* to the square root of a number of two decimal places to enable us to find the square root of a related number of three decimal places. This *addition* is always to the third decimal place since these mean differences in this case are thousandths.

All this will become clearer by considering the following examples.

Thus
$$\sqrt{5\cdot8} = 2\cdot408$$
$$\sqrt{5\cdot86} = 2\cdot421$$
$$\sqrt{5\cdot867} = 2\cdot421 + 0\cdot001 = 2\cdot422$$

or
$$\sqrt{6\cdot3} = 2\cdot510$$
$$\sqrt{6\cdot32} = 2\cdot514$$
$$\sqrt{6\cdot328} = 2\cdot514 + 0\cdot002 = 2\cdot516$$

Notice further that the following square roots can be derived from these:

$$\sqrt{0\cdot058} = 0\cdot2408; \qquad \sqrt{586} = 24\cdot21;$$
$$\sqrt{58,670} = 242\cdot2; \qquad \sqrt{0\cdot00063} = 0\cdot0251;$$
$$\sqrt{632} = 25\cdot14 \qquad \sqrt{0\cdot06328} = 0\cdot2516$$

Exercise 10f. *Oral*

Using the table on p. 125, (A) find the square root of each of the following numbers:

1. 5·7   2. 6·1   3. 6·4   4. 5·62   5. 5·85

(B) find the square root of:

6. 6·27   7. 6·37   8. 5·507   9. 5·619
10. 5·803   11. 6·194   12. 6·205   13. 0·00056
14. 587   15. 0·059   16. 62,400   17. 0·000005896
        18. 0·0006014   19. 631·8   20. 64,760

What has been said to enable us to use the small table on p. 125 can easily be extended to the more extensive range of numbers 1 to 100 given on pp. 128–31.

Check the accuracy of the following results, using this table:

$$\sqrt{1\cdot236} = 1\cdot112 \qquad \sqrt{4\cdot618} = 2\cdot149$$

$$\sqrt{8\cdot734} = 2\cdot956 \qquad \sqrt{17\cdot63} = 4\cdot199$$

$$\sqrt{38\cdot91} = 6\cdot238 \qquad \sqrt{54\cdot67} = 7\cdot394$$

$$\sqrt{40\cdot09} = 6\cdot332 \qquad \sqrt{80\cdot07} = 8\cdot948$$

$$\sqrt{71\cdot01} = 8\cdot427 \qquad \sqrt{93\cdot17} = 9\cdot653$$

Any number of not more than **four** significant figures can be brought within the range of our tables (1 to 100) and hence its square root can be found.

Example 10. Using the tables on pp. 128–31, find the square root of:

        (1) 7,893,000   (2) 9815
        (3) 0·7643   (4) 0·0005321

(1) $7,893,000 = 7\cdot893 . 10^6$

    $\therefore \ \sqrt{7,893,000} = 10^3 . \sqrt{7\cdot893} = 2,810$

(2) $9,815 = 98\cdot15 . 10^2$

    $\therefore \ \sqrt{9,815} = 10 \sqrt{98\cdot15} = 99\cdot07$

(3) $0\cdot7643 = 76\cdot43 \div 10^2$

    $\therefore \ \sqrt{0\cdot7643} = \frac{1}{10} \sqrt{76\cdot43} = 0\cdot8743$

(4) $0\cdot0005321 = 5\cdot321 \div 10^4$

    $\therefore \ \sqrt{0\cdot0005321} = \frac{1}{10^2} . \sqrt{5\cdot321} = 0\cdot02307$

EXERCISE 10G. *Oral*

Using the table on pp. 128–31, find the square root of each of the following numbers:

1. 3·65	**2.** 4·73	**3.** 7·615	**4.** 8·431
5. 15·37	**6.** 21·08	**7.** 46·15	**8.** 50·09
9. 69·58	**10.** 73·21	**11.** 80·19	**12.** 95·03
13. 0·2543	**14.** 0·3621	**15.** 0·06504	**16.** 0·07309
17. 0·002648	**18.** 0·003219	**19.** 0·0005726	**20.** 0·0006108
21. 786·9	**22.** 621·3	**23.** 790·8	**24.** 841·2
25. 3,861	**26.** 4,219	**27.** 59,530	**28.** 79,090
29. 693,100	**30.** 8,543,000		

SQUARE ROOTS. From 1 to 10

	0	1	2	3	4	5	6	7	8	9	Mean Difference 1 2 3	4 5 6	7 8
1·0	1·000	1·005	1·010	1·015	1·020	1·025	1·030	1·034	1·039	1·044	0 1 1	2 2 3	3 4
1·1	1·049	1·054	1·058	1·063	1·068	1·072	1·077	1·082	1·086	1·091	0 1 1	2 2 3	3 4
1·2	1·095	1·100	1·105	1·109	1·114	1·118	1·122	1·127	1·131	1·136	0 1 1	2 2 3	3 4
1·3	1·140	1·145	1·149	1·153	1·158	1·162	1·166	1·170	1·175	1·179	0 1 1	2 2 3	3 3
1·4	1·183	1·187	1·192	1·196	1·200	1·204	1·208	1·212	1·217	1·221	0 1 1	2 2 2	3 3
1·5	1·225	1·229	1·233	1·237	1·241	1·245	1·249	1·253	1·257	1·261	0 1 1	2 2 2	3 3
1·6	1·265	1·269	1·273	1·277	1·281	1·285	1·288	1·292	1·296	1·300	0 1 1	2 2 2	3 3
1·7	1·304	1·308	1·311	1·315	1·319	1·323	1·327	1·330	1·334	1·338	0 1 1	2 2 2	3 3
1·8	1·342	1·345	1·349	1·353	1·356	1·360	1·364	1·367	1·371	1·375	0 1 1	1 2 2	3 3
1·9	1·378	1·382	1·386	1·389	1·393	1·396	1·400	1·404	1·407	1·411	0 1 1	1 2 2	3 3
2·0	1·414	1·418	1·421	1·425	1·428	1·432	1·435	1·439	1·442	1·446	0 1 1	1 2 2	2 3
2·1	1·449	1·453	1·456	1·459	1·463	1·466	1·470	1·473	1·476	1·480	0 1 1	1 2 2	2 3
2·2	1·483	1·487	1·490	1·493	1·497	1·500	1·503	1·507	1·510	1·513	0 1 1	1 2 2	2 3
2·3	1·517	1·520	1·523	1·526	1·530	1·533	1·536	1·539	1·543	1·546	0 1 1	1 2 2	2 3
2·4	1·549	1·552	1·556	1·559	1·562	1·565	1·568	1·572	1·575	1·578	0 1 1	1 2 2	2 3
2·5	1·581	1·584	1·587	1·591	1·594	1·597	1·600	1·603	1·606	1·609	0 1 1	1 2 2	2 3
2·6	1·612	1·616	1·619	1·622	1·625	1·628	1·631	1·634	1·637	1·640	0 1 1	1 2 2	2 2
2·7	1·643	1·646	1·649	1·652	1·655	1·658	1·661	1·664	1·667	1·670	0 1 1	1 2 2	2 2
2·8	1·673	1·676	1·679	1·682	1·685	1·688	1·691	1·694	1·697	1·700	0 1 1	1 1 2	2 2
2·9	1·703	1·706	1·709	1·712	1·715	1·718	1·720	1·723	1·726	1·729	0 1 1	1 1 2	2 2
3·0	1·732	1·735	1·738	1·741	1·744	1·746	1·749	1·752	1·755	1·758	0 1 1	1 1 2	2 2
3·1	1·761	1·764	1·766	1·769	1·772	1·775	1·778	1·780	1·783	1·786	0 1 1	1 1 2	2 2
3·2	1·789	1·792	1·794	1·797	1·800	1·803	1·806	1·808	1·811	1·814	0 1 1	1 1 2	2 2
3·3	1·817	1·819	1·822	1·825	1·828	1·830	1·833	1·836	1·838	1·841	0 1 1	1 1 2	2 2
3·4	1·844	1·847	1·849	1·852	1·855	1·857	1·860	1·863	1·865	1·868	0 1 1	1 1 2	2 2
3·5	1·871	1·873	1·876	1·879	1·881	1·884	1·887	1·889	1·892	1·895	0 1 1	1 1 2	2 2
3·6	1·897	1·900	1·903	1·905	1·908	1·910	1·913	1·916	1·918	1·921	0 1 1	1 1 2	2 2
3·7	1·924	1·926	1·929	1·931	1·934	1·936	1·939	1·942	1·944	1·947	0 1 1	1 1 2	2 2
3·8	1·949	1·952	1·954	1·957	1·960	1·962	1·965	1·967	1·970	1·972	0 1 1	1 1 2	2 2
3·9	1·975	1·977	1·980	1·982	1·985	1·987	1·990	1·992	1·995	1·997	0 1 1	1 1 2	2 2
4·0	2·000	2·002	2·005	2·007	2·010	2·012	2·015	2·017	2·020	2·022	0 0 1	1 1 1	2 2
4·1	2·025	2·027	2·030	2·032	2·035	2·037	2·040	2·042	2·045	2·047	0 0 1	1 1 1	2 2
4·2	2·049	2·052	2·054	2·057	2·059	2·062	2·064	2·066	2·069	2·071	0 0 1	1 1 1	2 2
4·3	2·074	2·076	2·078	2·081	2·083	2·086	2·088	2·090	2·093	2·095	0 0 1	1 1 1	2 2
4·4	2·098	2·100	2·102	2·105	2·107	2·110	2·112	2·114	2·117	2·119	0 0 1	1 1 1	2 2
4·5	2·121	2·124	2·126	2·128	2·131	2·133	2·135	2·138	2·140	2·142	0 0 1	1 1 1	2 2
4·6	2·145	2·147	2·149	2·152	2·154	2·156	2·159	2·161	2·163	2·166	0 0 1	1 1 1	2 2
4·7	2·168	2·170	2·173	2·175	2·177	2·179	2·182	2·184	2·186	2·189	0 0 1	1 1 1	2 2
4·8	2·191	2·193	2·195	2·198	2·200	2·202	2·205	2·207	2·209	2·211	0 0 1	1 1 1	2 2
4·9	2·214	2·216	2·218	2·220	2·223	2·225	2·227	2·229	2·232	2·234	0 0 1	1 1 1	2 2
5·0	2·236	2·238	2·241	2·243	2·245	2·247	2·249	2·252	2·254	2·256	0 0 1	1 1 1	2 2
5·1	2·258	2·261	2·263	2·265	2·267	2·269	2·272	2·274	2·276	2·278	0 0 1	1 1 1	2 2
5·2	2·280	2·283	2·285	2·287	2·289	2·291	2·293	2·296	2·298	2·300	0 0 1	1 1 1	2 2
5·3	2·302	2·304	2·307	2·309	2·311	2·313	2·315	2·317	2·319	2·322	0 0 1	1 1 1	2 2
5·4	2·324	2·326	2·328	2·330	2·332	2·335	2·337	2·339	2·341	2·343	0 0 1	1 1 1	1 2 2

	0	1	2	3	4	5	6	7	8	9	Mean Differences 1 2 3	4 5 6	7 8 9
5·5	2·345	2·347	2·349	2·352	2·354	2·356	2·358	2·360	2·362	2·364	0 0 1	1 1 1	1 2 2
5·6	2·366	2·369	2·371	2·373	2·375	2·377	2·379	2·381	2·383	2·385	0 0 1	1 1 1	1 2 2
5·7	2·387	2·390	2·392	2·394	2·396	2·398	2·400	2·402	2·404	2·406	0 0 1	1 1 1	1 2 2
5·8	2·408	2·410	2·412	2·415	2·417	2·419	2·421	2·423	2·425	2·427	0 0 1	1 1 1	1 2 2
5·9	2·429	2·431	2·433	2·435	2·437	2·439	2·441	2·443	2·445	2·447	0 0 1	1 1 1	1 2 2
6·0	2·449	2·452	2·454	2·456	2·458	2·460	2·462	2·464	2·466	2·468	0 0 1	1 1 1	1 2 2
6·1	2·470	2·472	2·474	2·476	2·478	2·480	2·482	2·484	2·486	2·488	0 0 1	1 1 1	1 2 2
6·2	2·490	2·492	2·494	2·496	2·498	2·500	2·502	2·504	2·506	2·508	0 0 1	1 1 1	1 2 2
6·3	2·510	2·512	2·514	2·516	2·518	2·520	2·522	2·524	2·526	2·528	0 0 1	1 1 1	1 2 2
6·4	2·530	2·532	2·534	2·536	2·538	2·540	2·542	2·544	2·546	2·548	0 0 1	1 1 1	1 2 2
6·5	2·550	2·551	2·553	2·555	2·557	2·559	2·561	2·563	2·565	2·567	0 0 1	1 1 1	1 2 2
6·6	2·569	2·571	2·573	2·575	2·577	2·579	2·581	2·583	2·585	2·587	0 0 1	1 1 1	1 2 2
6·7	2·588	2·590	2·592	2·594	2·596	2·598	2·600	2·602	2·604	2·606	0 0 1	1 1 1	1 2 2
6·8	2·608	2·610	2·612	2·613	2·615	2·617	2·619	2·621	2·623	2·625	0 0 1	1 1 1	1 2 2
6·9	2·627	2·629	2·631	2·632	2·634	2·636	2·638	2·640	2·642	2·644	0 0 1	1 1 1	1 2 2
7·0	2·646	2·648	2·650	2·651	2·653	2·655	2·657	2·659	2·661	2·663	0 0 1	1 1 1	1 2 2
7·1	2·665	2·666	2·668	2·670	2·672	2·674	2·676	2·678	2·680	2·681	0 0 1	1 1 1	1 1 2
7·2	2·683	2·685	2·687	2·689	2·691	2·693	2·694	2·696	2·698	2·700	0 0 1	1 1 1	1 1 2
7·3	2·702	2·704	2·706	2·707	2·709	2·711	2·713	2·715	2·717	2·718	0 0 1	1 1 1	1 1 2
7·4	2·720	2·722	2·724	2·726	2·728	2·729	2·731	2·733	2·735	2·737	0 0 1	1 1 1	1 1 2
7·5	2·739	2·740	2·742	2·744	2·746	2·748	2·750	2·751	2·753	2·755	0 0 1	1 1 1	1 1 2
7·6	2·757	2·759	2·760	2·762	2·764	2·766	2·768	2·769	2·771	2·773	0 0 1	1 1 1	1 1 2
7·7	2·775	2·777	2·778	2·780	2·782	2·784	2·786	2·787	2·789	2·791	0 0 1	1 1 1	1 1 2
7·8	2·793	2·795	2·796	2·798	2·800	2·802	2·804	2·805	2·807	2·809	0 0 1	1 1 1	1 1 2
7·9	2·811	2·812	2·814	2·816	2·818	2·820	2·821	2·823	2·825	2·827	0 0 1	1 1 1	1 1 2
8·0	2·828	2·830	2·832	2·834	2·835	2·837	2·839	2·841	2·843	2·844	0 0 1	1 1 1	1 1 2
8·1	2·846	2·848	2·850	2·851	2·853	2·855	2·857	2·858	2·860	2·862	0 0 1	1 1 1	1 1 2
8·2	2·864	2·865	2·867	2·869	2·871	2·872	2·874	2·876	2·877	2·879	0 0 1	1 1 1	1 1 2
8·3	2·881	2·883	2·884	2·886	2·888	2·890	2·891	2·893	2·895	2·897	0 0 1	1 1 1	1 1 2
8·4	2·898	2·900	2·902	2·903	2·905	2·907	2·909	2·910	2·912	2·914	0 0 1	1 1 1	1 1 2
8·5	2·915	2·917	2·919	2·921	2·922	2·924	2·926	2·927	2·929	2·931	0 0 1	1 1 1	1 1 2
8·6	2·933	2·934	2·936	2·938	2·939	2·941	2·943	2·944	2·946	2·948	0 0 1	1 1 1	1 1 2
8·7	2·950	2·951	2·953	2·955	2·956	2·958	2·960	2·961	2·963	2·965	0 0 1	1 1 1	1 1 2
8·8	2·966	2·968	2·970	2·972	2·973	2·975	2·977	2·978	2·980	2·982	0 0 1	1 1 1	1 1 2
8·9	2·983	2·985	2·987	2·988	2·990	2·992	2·993	2·995	2·997	2·998	0 0 1	1 1 1	1 1 2
9·0	3·000	3·002	3·003	3·005	3·007	3·008	3·010	3·012	3·013	3·015	0 0 0	1 1 1	1 1 1
9·1	3·017	3·018	3·020	3·022	3·023	3·025	3·027	3·028	3·030	3·032	0 0 0	1 1 1	1 1 1
9·2	3·033	3·035	3·036	3·038	3·040	3·041	3·043	3·045	3·046	3·048	0 0 0	1 1 1	1 1 1
9·3	3·050	3·051	3·053	3·055	3·056	3·058	3·059	3·061	3·063	3·064	0 0 0	1 1 1	1 1 1
9·4	3·066	3·068	3·069	3·071	3·072	3·074	3·076	3·077	3·079	3·081	0 0 0	1 1 1	1 1 1
9·5	3·082	3·084	3·085	3·087	3·089	3·090	3·092	3·094	3·095	3·097	0 0 0	1 1 1	1 1 1
9·6	3·098	3·100	3·102	3·103	3·105	3·106	3·108	3·110	3·111	3·113	0 0 0	1 1 1	1 1 1
9·7	3·114	3·116	3·118	3·119	3·121	3·122	3·124	3·126	3·127	3·129	0 0 0	1 1 1	1 1 1
9·8	3·130	3·132	3·134	3·135	3·137	3·138	3·140	3·142	3·143	3·145	0 0 0	1 1 1	1 1 1
9·9	3·146	3·148	3·150	3·151	3·153	3·154	3·156	3·158	3·159	3·161	0 0 0	1 1 1	1 1 1

	0	1	2	3	4	5	6	7	8	9	Mean Differences 1 2 3	4 5 6	7 8
10	3·162	3·178	3·194	3·209	3·225	3·240	3·256	3·271	3·286	3·302	2 3 5	6 8 9	11 12
11	3·317	3·332	3·347	3·362	3·376	3·391	3·406	3·421	3·435	3·450	1 3 4	6 7 9	10 12
12	3·464	3·479	3·493	3·507	3·521	3·536	3·550	3·564	3·578	3·592	1 3 4	6 7 8	10 11
13	3·606	3·619	3·633	3·647	3·661	3·674	3·688	3·701	3·715	3·728	1 3 4	5 7 8	10 11
14	3·742	3·755	3·768	3·782	3·795	3·808	3·821	3·834	3·847	3·860	1 3 4	5 7 8	9 11
15	3·873	3·886	3·899	3·912	3·924	3·937	3·950	3·962	3·975	3·987	1 3 4	5 6 8	9 10
16	4·000	4·012	4·025	4·037	4·050	4·062	4·074	4·087	4·099	4·111	1 2 4	5 6 7	9 10
17	4·123	4·135	4·147	4·159	4·171	4·183	4·195	4·207	4·219	4·231	1 2 4	5 6 7	8 10
18	4·243	4·254	4·266	4·278	4·290	4·301	4·313	4·324	4·336	4·347	1 2 3	5 6 7	8 9
19	4·359	4·370	4·382	4·393	4·405	4·416	4·427	4·438	4·450	4·461	1 2 3	5 6 7	8 9
20	4·472	4·483	4·494	4·506	4·517	4·528	4·539	4·550	4·561	4·572	1 2 3	4 6 7	8 9
21	4·583	4·593	4·604	4·615	4·626	4·637	4·648	4·658	4·669	4·680	1 2 3	4 5 6	8 9
22	4·690	4·701	4·712	4·722	4·733	4·743	4·754	4·764	4·775	4·785	1 2 3	4 5 6	7 8
23	4·796	4·806	4·817	4·827	4·837	4·848	4·858	4·868	4·879	4·889	1 2 3	4 5 6	7 8
24	4·899	4·909	4·919	4·930	4·940	4·950	4·960	4·970	4·980	4·990	1 2 3	4 5 6	7 8
25	5·000	5·010	5·020	5·030	5·040	5·050	5·060	5·070	5·079	5·089	1 2 3	4 5 6	7 8
26	5·099	5·109	5·119	5·128	5·138	5·148	5·158	5·167	5·177	5·187	1 2 3	4 5 6	7 8
27	5·196	5·206	5·215	5·225	5·235	5·244	5·254	5·263	5·273	5·282	1 2 3	4 5 6	7 8
28	5·292	5·301	5·310	5·320	5·329	5·339	5·348	5·357	5·367	5·376	1 2 3	4 5 6	7 7
29	5·385	5·394	5·404	5·413	5·422	5·431	5·441	5·450	5·459	5·468	1 2 3	4 5 5	6 7
30	5·477	5·486	5·495	5·505	5·514	5·523	5·532	5·541	5·550	5·559	1 2 3	4 4 5	6 7
31	5·568	5·577	5·586	5·595	5·604	5·612	5·621	5·630	5·639	5·648	1 2 3	3 4 5	6 7
32	5·657	5·666	5·675	5·683	5·692	5·701	5·710	5·718	5·727	5·736	1 2 3	3 4 5	6 7
33	5·745	5·753	5·762	5·771	5·779	5·788	5·797	5·805	5·814	5·822	1 2 3	3 4 5	6 7
34	5·831	5·840	5·848	5·857	5·865	5·874	5·882	5·891	5·899	5·908	1 2 3	3 4 5	6 7
35	5·916	5·925	5·933	5·941	5·950	5·958	5·967	5·975	5·983	5·992	1 2 2	3 4 5	6 7
36	6·000	6·008	6·017	6·025	6·033	6·042	6·050	6·058	6·066	6·075	1 2 2	3 4 5	6 7
37	6·083	6·091	6·099	6·107	6·116	6·124	6·132	6·140	6·148	6·156	1 2 2	3 4 5	6 7
38	6·164	6·173	6·181	6·189	6·197	6·205	6·213	6·221	6·229	6·237	1 2 2	3 4 5	6 6
39	6·245	6·253	6·261	6·269	6·277	6·285	6·293	6·301	6·309	6·317	1 2 2	3 4 5	6 6
40	6·325	6·332	6·340	6·348	6·356	6·364	6·372	6·380	6·387	6·395	1 2 2	3 4 5	6 6
41	6·403	6·411	6·419	6·427	6·434	6·442	6·450	6·458	6·465	6·473	1 2 2	3 4 5	5 6
42	6·481	6·488	6·496	6·504	6·512	6·519	6·527	6·535	6·542	6·550	1 2 2	3 4 5	5 6
43	6·557	6·565	6·573	6·580	6·588	6·595	6·603	6·611	6·618	6·626	1 2 2	3 4 5	5 6
44	6·633	6·641	6·648	6·656	6·663	6·671	6·678	6·686	6·693	6·701	1 2 2	3 4 5	6 7
45	6·708	6·716	6·723	6·731	6·738	6·745	6·753	6·760	6·768	6·775	1 1 2	3 4 4	5 6
46	6·782	6·790	6·797	6·804	6·812	6·819	6·826	6·834	6·841	6·848	1 1 2	3 4 4	5 6
47	6·856	6·863	6·870	6·877	6·885	6·892	6·899	6·907	6·914	6·921	1 1 2	3 4 4	5 6
48	6·928	6·935	6·943	6·950	6·957	6·964	6·971	6·979	6·986	6·993	1 1 2	3 4 4	5 6
49	7·000	7·007	7·014	7·021	7·029	7·036	7·043	7·050	7·057	7·064	1 1 2	3 4 4	5 6
50	7·071	7·078	7·085	7·092	7·099	7·106	7·113	7·120	7·127	7·134	1 1 2	3 4 4	5 6
51	7·141	7·148	7·155	7·162	7·169	7·176	7·183	7·190	7·197	7·204	1 1 2	3 4 4	5 6
52	7·211	7·218	7·225	7·232	7·239	7·246	7·253	7·259	7·266	7·273	1 1 2	3 3 4	5 6
53	7·280	7·287	7·294	7·301	7·308	7·314	7·321	7·328	7·335	7·342	1 1 2	3 3 4	5 6
54	7·348	7·355	7·362	7·369	7·376	7·382	7·389	7·396	7·403	7·409	1 1 2	3 3 4	5 6

SQUARE ROOTS. From 10 to 100

	0	1	2	3	4	5	6	7	8	9	1 2 3	4 5 6	7 8 9
55	7·416	7·423	7·430	7·436	7·443	7·450	7·457	7·463	7·470	7·477	1 1 2	3 3 4	5 5 6
56	7·483	7·490	7·497	7·503	7·510	7·517	7·523	7·530	7·537	7·543	1 1 2	3 3 4	5 5 6
57	7·550	7·556	7·563	7·570	7·576	7·583	7·589	7·596	7·603	7·609	1 1 2	3 3 4	5 5 6
58	7·616	7·622	7·629	7·635	7·642	7·649	7·655	7·662	7·668	7·675	1 1 2	3 3 4	5 5 6
59	7·681	7·688	7·694	7·701	7·707	7·714	7·720	7·727	7·733	7·740	1 1 2	3 3 4	4 5 6
60	7·746	7·752	7·759	7·765	7·772	7·778	7·785	7·791	7·797	7·804	1 1 2	3 3 4	4 5 6
61	7·810	7·817	7·823	7·829	7·836	7·842	7·849	7·855	7·861	7·868	1 1 2	3 3 4	4 5 6
62	7·874	7·880	7·887	7·893	7·899	7·906	7·912	7·918	7·925	7·931	1 1 2	3 3 4	4 5 6
63	7·937	7·944	7·950	7·956	7·962	7·969	7·975	7·981	7·987	7·994	1 1 2	3 3 4	4 5 6
64	8·000	8·006	8·012	8·019	8·025	8·031	8·037	8·044	8·050	8·056	1 1 2	2 3 4	4 5 6
65	8·062	8·068	8·075	8·081	8·087	8·093	8·099	8·106	8·112	8·118	1 1 2	2 3 4	4 5 6
66	8·124	8·130	8·136	8·142	8·149	8·155	8·161	8·167	8·173	8·179	1 1 2	2 3 4	4 5 5
67	8·185	8·191	8·198	8·204	8·210	8·216	8·222	8·228	8·234	8·240	1 1 2	2 3 4	4 5 5
68	8·246	8·252	8·258	8·264	8·270	8·276	8·283	8·289	8·295	8·301	1 1 2	2 3 4	4 5 5
69	8·307	8·313	8·319	8·325	8·331	8·337	8·343	8·349	8·355	8·361	1 1 2	2 3 4	4 5 5
70	8·367	8·373	8·379	8·385	8·390	8·396	8·402	8·408	8·414	8·420	1 1 2	2 3 4	4 5 5
71	8·426	8·432	8·438	8·444	8·450	8·456	8·462	8·468	8·473	8·479	1 1 2	2 3 4	4 5 5
72	8·485	8·491	8·497	8·503	8·509	8·515	8·521	8·526	8·532	8·538	1 1 2	2 3 3	4 5 5
73	8·544	8·550	8·556	8·562	8·567	8·573	8·579	8·585	8·591	8·597	1 1 2	2 3 3	4 5 5
74	8·602	8·608	8·614	8·620	8·626	8·631	8·637	8·643	8·649	8·654	1 1 2	2 3 3	4 5 5
75	8·660	8·666	8·672	8·678	8·683	8·689	8·695	8·701	8·706	8·712	1 1 2	2 3 3	4 5 5
76	8·718	8·724	8·729	8·735	8·741	8·746	8·752	8·758	8·764	8·769	1 1 2	2 3 3	4 5 5
77	8·775	8·781	8·786	8·792	8·798	8·803	8·809	8·815	8·820	8·826	1 1 2	2 3 3	4 4 5
78	8·832	8·837	8·843	8·849	8·854	8·860	8·866	8·871	8·877	8·883	1 1 2	2 3 3	4 4 5
79	8·888	8·894	8·899	8·905	8·911	8·916	8·922	8·927	8·933	8·939	1 1 2	2 3 3	4 4 5
80	8·944	8·950	8·955	8·961	8·967	8·972	8·978	8·983	8·989	8·994	1 1 2	2 3 3	4 4 5
81	9·000	9·006	9·011	9·017	9·022	9·028	9·033	9·039	9·044	9·050	1 1 2	2 3 3	4 4 5
82	9·055	9·061	9·066	9·072	9·077	9·083	9·088	9·094	9·099	9·105	1 1 2	2 3 3	4 4 5
83	9·110	9·116	9·121	9·127	9·132	9·138	9·143	9·149	9·154	9·160	1 1 2	2 3 3	4 4 5
84	9·165	9·171	9·176	9·182	9·187	9·192	9·198	9·203	9·209	9·214	1 1 2	2 3 3	4 4 5
85	9·220	9·225	9·230	9·236	9·241	9·247	9·252	9·257	9·263	9·268	1 1 2	2 3 3	4 4 5
86	9·274	9·279	9·284	9·290	9·295	9·301	9·306	9·311	9·317	9·322	1 1 2	2 3 3	4 4 5
87	9·327	9·333	9·338	9·343	9·349	9·354	9·359	9·365	9·370	9·375	1 1 2	2 3 3	4 4 5
88	9·381	9·386	9·391	9·397	9·402	9·407	9·413	9·418	9·423	9·429	1 1 2	2 3 3	4 4 5
89	9·434	9·439	9·445	9·450	9·455	9·460	9·466	9·471	9·476	9·482	1 1 2	2 3 3	4 4 5
90	9·487	9·492	9·497	9·503	9·508	9·513	9·518	9·524	9·529	9·534	1 1 2	2 3 3	4 4 5
91	9·539	9·545	9·550	9·555	9·560	9·566	9·571	9·576	9·581	9·586	1 1 2	2 3 3	4 4 5
92	9·592	9·597	9·602	9·607	9·612	9·618	9·623	9·628	9·633	9·638	1 1 2	2 3 3	4 4 5
93	9·644	9·649	9·654	9·659	9·664	9·670	9·675	9·680	9·685	9·690	1 1 2	2 3 3	4 4 5
94	9·695	9·701	9·706	9·711	9·716	9·721	9·726	9·731	9·737	9·742	1 1 2	2 3 3	4 4 5
95	9·747	9·752	9·757	9·762	9·767	9·772	9·778	9·783	9·788	9·793	1 1 2	2 3 3	4 4 5
96	9·798	9·803	9·808	9·813	9·818	9·823	9·829	9·834	9·839	9·844	1 1 2	2 3 3	4 4 5
97	9·849	9·854	9·859	9·864	9·869	9·874	9·879	9·884	9·889	9·894	1 1 1	2 3 3	4 4 5
98	9·899	9·905	9·910	9·915	9·920	9·925	9·930	9·935	9·940	9·945	0 1 1	2 2 3	3 4 4
99	9·950	9·955	9·960	9·965	9·970	9·975	9·980	9·985	9·990	9·995	0 1 1	2 2 3	3 4 4

Square Root. Problems

Example 11. Find the perimeter of a 10-acre square field.

Area of field = 10 acres = 48,400 sq. yd.

∴ Length of side = $\sqrt{48,400}$ yd.

= 220 yd.

∴ Perimeter of field = 220 × 4 yd.

= 880 yd.

Example 12. A rectangular garden contains 800 sq. yd. and the length is twice the breadth. What will be the cost of fencing it at 8*s.* 6*d.* per yd?

Let length of garden = 2*x* yd.

Then breadth of garden = *x* yd.

∴ Area of garden = $2x^2$ sq. yd.

But area of garden = 800 sq. yd.

∴ $2x^2 = 800$

∴ $x^2 = 400$

∴ $x = 20$

∴ Length of garden = 40 yd.

Breadth of garden = 20 yd.

∴ Perimeter of garden = 2(40 + 20) yd.

= 120 yd.

1 yd. of fencing costs 8*s*. 6*d*.
∴ 120 yd. of fencing costs 8*s*. 6*d*. × 120
i.e. £51

EXERCISE 10H

1. Find the perimeter of a square field of area 64,009 sq. yd.

2. A square courtyard is paved with tiles, each 4 in. square. If 253,009 tiles are used, what is the length of a side of the courtyard?

3. How long will it take a man to walk round the boundary of a square field containing 90 acres at the rate of 5 ml. per hr.?

4. A square field has an area of $5\frac{5}{8}$ acres. Find the cost of putting a fence round the field at 1*s*. $7\frac{1}{2}d$. per yd.

5. A square field has an area of 12 acres 4,420 sq. yd. Find the cost of fencing it at 2*s*. 8*d*. per yd.

6. The cost of fencing a square field of area 9 acres 540 sq. yd. is £147. Find the cost of fencing per yard.

7. A man takes 13 min. 20 sec. to walk round a square field 40 acres in area. Find his speed in miles per hour.

8. A square metal plate weighs 686 lb. If the metal weighs $31\frac{1}{2}$ lb. per sq. ft., calculate the length of a side of the plate.

9. The total area of the six faces of a cube is 30 sq. ft. 54 sq. in. Find the weight of the cube in lb., oz., if a cubic foot of it weighs 2,000 oz.

10. A square playing field of area $22\frac{1}{2}$ acres is to be fenced and planted with grass. If the cost of fencing is 2*s*. 6*d*. a yard and of seed-planting $1\frac{1}{2}d$. a square yard, find the total cost.

11. A square lawn is bordered by a path $4\frac{1}{2}$ ft. wide; the path and lawn together occupying $\frac{1}{10}$ of an acre. Find the cost of paving the path with bricks at 6*s*. 3*d*. per sq. yd.

12. A square garden plot of side 29 yd. has a uniform path round it. If the area of the path is 315 sq. yd., find the width of the path.

13. Walking at 3 ml. per hr. a farmer finds that he takes 6 min. to walk along one side of a rectangular field and 17 minutes to walk all round it.

Find (i) the area of the field in acres; and (ii) the time to walk diagonally across the field at the same rate.

14. The length of a rectangular park is three times its breadth and its area is $7\frac{1}{2}$ acres. Find the cost of fencing it at 3*s*. 9*d*. per yd.

15. The area of a rectangular field is 26 acres 1,609 sq. yd. If its length is $2\frac{1}{4}$ times its breadth, find its perimeter. How long will it take a runner to run 22 times round the field at 10 ml. per hr.?

Ratio and Proportion

The **ratio** of one quantity to another of the same kind is the fraction that the first quantity is of the second.

Note, (i) it is essential that the two quantities be of the **same kind**;
(ii) sometimes the 'fraction' may be of the form $\frac{2}{1}$, i.e. a whole number.

Consider the expression $\dfrac{\text{£3 } 10s.}{\text{£2 } 5s.}$

This indicates:

(a) the number of times that £3 10s. contains £2 5s;
(b) the number expressing £3 10s. in terms of £2 5s. as unit;
(c) the measure of £3 10s. in terms of £2 5s.;
(d) the quotient when £3 10s. is divided by £2 5s.;
(e) the fraction which £3 10s. is of £2 5s.;
(f) the **ratio** of £3 10s. to £2 5s.

These will serve to illustrate the wide application of Ratio to arithmetical processes.

To find a Ratio

Example 1. Find the ratio of £3 10s. to £2 5s.

$$\text{Ratio} = \frac{\text{£3 } 10s.}{\text{£2 } 5s.} = \frac{\text{£}3\frac{1}{2}}{\text{£}2\frac{1}{4}} = \frac{7}{2} \times \frac{\overset{2}{\cancel{4}}}{\underset{1}{9}} = \frac{14}{9}$$

∴ Ratio is 14 : 9

Notice that in this work,

(i) the colon (:) is frequently used to indicate a ratio;

(ii) a ratio, being a fraction, **never** has units (£'s; ft.; lb., etc.)
tacked on to it.

Example 2.   Show that $\dfrac{4s.\ 3d.}{2s.\ 10d.} = \dfrac{3\ \text{cwt.}\ 3\ \text{qr.}}{2\ \text{cwt.}\ 56\ \text{lb.}}$

1st ratio $= \dfrac{4s.\ 3d}{2s.\ 10d.} = \dfrac{51d.}{34d.} = \tfrac{3}{2}$

2nd ratio $= \dfrac{3\ \text{cwt.}\ 3\ \text{qr.}}{2\ \text{cwt.}\ 56\ \text{lb.}} = \dfrac{3\tfrac{3}{4}\ \text{cwt.}}{2\tfrac{1}{2}\ \text{cwt.}} = \dfrac{15}{4} \times \dfrac{2}{5} = \tfrac{3}{2}$

$\therefore \dfrac{4s.\ 3d.}{2s.\ 10d.} = \dfrac{3\ \text{cwt.}\ 3\ \text{qr.}}{2\ \text{cwt.}\ 56\ \text{lb.}}$

EXERCISE 11A

Find the ratio of the following quantities to each other:

1. 27 to 36
2. 35 to 75
3. $2\tfrac{1}{2}$ to $3\tfrac{3}{4}$
4. $4\tfrac{1}{3}$ to $5\tfrac{1}{5}$
5. 3·78 to 4·41
6. 4·625 to 7·875
7. £1 2s. 6d. to £4
8. 10s. 6d. to 15s.
9. 5s. 10d. to £1 4s. 6d.
10. £3 4s. to £10 13s. 4d.
11. 2 lb. 13 oz. to 3 lb. 12 oz.
12. 1 cwt. 1 qr. to 3 cwt. 14 lb.
13. 1 ton 6 cwt. to 3 tons 5 cwt.
14. 5 yd. 5 in. to 9 yd. 9 in.
15. 2 ml. 6 fur. 200 yd. to 3 ml. 320 yd.
16. 2 sq. ft. 16 sq. in. to 4 sq. ft. 108 sq. in.
17. 5 cub. yd. 15 cub. ft. to 9 cub. yd. 12 cub. ft.
18. 4·2 Km. to 3 ml. (1 Km. = $\tfrac{5}{8}$ ml.)

Simplify the following ratios:

19. $\dfrac{11s.\ 8d.}{18s.\ 11\tfrac{1}{2}d.}$
20. $\dfrac{£1\ 6s.\ 0\tfrac{1}{2}d.}{£1\ 16s.\ 5\tfrac{1}{2}d.}$
21. $\dfrac{1\ \text{cwt.}\ 45\ \text{lb.}\ 8\ \text{oz.}}{3\ \text{cwt.}\ 2\ \text{qr.}\ 1\ \text{lb.}\ 12\ \text{oz.}}$
22. $\dfrac{1\ \text{ml.}\ 2\ \text{fur.}\ 50\ \text{yd.}}{1\ \text{ml.}\ 7\ \text{fur.}\ 75\ \text{yd.}}$

Prove that:

23. $\dfrac{1\ \text{cwt.}\ 5\ \text{lb.}}{4\ \text{cwt.}\ 2\ \text{lb.}} = \dfrac{7s.\ 0\tfrac{1}{2}d.}{£1\ 7s.\ 1d.}$
24. $\dfrac{134\ \text{yd.}\ 1\ \text{ft.}\ 4\ \text{in.}}{\tfrac{1}{3}\ \text{mile}} = \dfrac{3s.\ 2\tfrac{1}{2}d.}{14s.}$
25. $\dfrac{1\ \text{qr.}\ 7\ \text{lb.}\ 7\ \text{oz.}}{2\ \text{qr.}\ 3\ \text{lb.}\ 1\ \text{oz.}} = \dfrac{2\ \text{fur.}\ 1\ \text{yd.}}{3\ \text{fur.}\ 3\ \text{ch.}\ 9\ \text{yd.}}$

Given a Ratio and a Quantity to find Another Quantity

Example 3. Find what sum bears to £1 8s. 4d. the ratio of 3 to 4.

$$\frac{\text{Required sum}}{£1\ 8s.\ 4d.} = \frac{3}{4}$$

∴ Required sum $= \frac{3}{4}$ of £1 8s. 4d.
$$= 3 \times 7s.\ 1d.$$
$$= £1\ 1s.\ 3d.$$

Example 4. Find what weight bears to 2 cwt. 1 qr. 7 lb. the same ratio as 7s. 4d. bears to £1 5s. 8d.

$$\text{Given ratio} = \frac{7s.\ 4d.}{£1\ 5s.\ 8d.} = \frac{7\frac{1}{3}s.}{25\frac{2}{3}s.} = \frac{\overset{2}{\cancel{22}}}{\underset{1}{\cancel{3}}} \times \frac{\overset{1}{\cancel{3}}}{\underset{7}{\cancel{77}}} = \frac{2}{7}$$

∴ $\dfrac{\text{Required weight}}{\text{2 cwt. 1 qr. 7 lb.}} = \frac{2}{7}$

∴ Required weight $= \frac{2}{7}$ of 9 qr. 7 lb.

$$= \frac{2}{\cancel{7}} \times \frac{\overset{37}{\cancel{259}}}{1} \text{ lb.}$$

$$= 74 \text{ lb.}$$
$$= 2 \text{ qr. } 18 \text{ lb.}$$

EXERCISE 11B

1. What sum bears to 11s. $5\frac{1}{2}d.$ the ratio of 7 to 11?

2. The sum £1 13s. 3d. bears to another sum the ratio of 2 to 3. Find this sum.

3. The weight 1 cwt. 31 lb. 4 oz. bears to another weight the ratio of 3 to 4. Find this weight.

4. What weight bears to 4 cwt. 3 qr. $20\frac{1}{2}$ lb. the ratio of 7 to 8?

5. What distance bears to 18 yd. 2 ft. 3 in. the ratio of 7 to 9?

6. The area 2 sq. ft. 90 sq. in. bears to another area the ratio of 2 to 7. Find this area.

7. What sum bears to 14s. $2\frac{1}{2}d.$ the same ratio as £2 6s. 3d. bears to £4 4s. $9\frac{1}{2}d.$?

8. What distance bears to 4 fur. 110 yd. the same ratio as 1 ton 8 cwt. 3 qr. bears to 3 tons 3 cwt. 1 qr.?

9. What sum bears to £1 1s. 5½d. the same ratio as 1 qr. 4 lb. 6 oz. bears to 1 qr. 18 lb. 4 oz.?

10. The weight 5 cwt. 4 st. 5 lb. bears to another weight the same ratio as 7 sq. ft. 15 sq. in. bears to 11 sq. ft. 121 sq. in. Find this weight.

The Unitary Method

Many pairs of quantities are so connected with each other that when one of them is doubled, trebled, halved or multiplied by any number, then the other is also doubled, trebled, halved or multiplied by the **same** number.

e.g. price of 3 lb. of tea = 3 times the price of 1 lb. of tea

,, ,, ¾ lb. ,, ,, = ¾ ,, ,, ,, ,, ,, ,, ,, ,,

Quantities which are connected in this way are said (i) to be *directly proportional* to each other or (ii) to *vary directly* with each other.

In dealing with such quantities it is frequently useful to reduce one of them to **unity**. Hence this method.

Example 5. If 13 cwt. of material cost £8 9s., what will 48 cwt. cost?

13 cwt. of material cost £8 9s., i.e. 169s.

$$\therefore \text{ 1 cwt. ,, ,, costs } \frac{169s.}{13} = 13s.$$

$$\therefore \text{ 48 cwt. ,, ,, cost } 13s. \times 48$$

$$= 624s.$$

$$= £31 \ 4s.$$

Other pairs of quantities are so connected with each other, that when one of them is doubled, trebled, halved or multiplied by any number, then the other is halved, divided by three, doubled or divided by the same number.

Quantities which are connected in this way are said (i) to be *inversely proportional* to each other or (ii) to *vary inversely* with each other.

Example 6. If 4 men can do a job in 24 hours, how many men can do it in 16 hours?

24 hr. is time taken for job by 4 men

∴ 1 hr. ,, ,,   ,,   ,,   ,,   ,, 4×24 men

∴ 16 hr. ,, ,,   ,,   ,,   ,,   ,, $\dfrac{\overset{1}{\cancel{4}} \times \overset{6}{\cancel{24}}}{\underset{\underset{1}{\cancel{4}}}{\cancel{16}}}$ men

= 6 men

Exercise 11c

1. If 8 lb. of coffee cost £3 6s. 8d., how much will 5 lb. cost?

2. If the 2nd class railway fare for 88 miles is 18s. 4d., what is the 2nd class railway fare for 20 miles reckoned at the same rate?

3. If 8 tractors can plough 280 acres in a certain time, how many acres can 11 tractors plough in the same time?

4. If 5 tractors can plough a field in 7 days, in how many days could 7 tractors plough the same field?

5. A man walks 85 miles in 20 hours; in how many hours will he walk 68 miles at the same pace?

6. If 17 men can do a piece of work in 374 days, how many days should 11 men take for the same work?

7. If 27 men can build a wall in 35 hours, how many men could build it in 5 days of 9 hours each?

8. A train does a journey in $4\frac{1}{2}$ hours travelling at the rate of 35 miles per hour; how long would it have taken for the same journey travelling at the rate of 56 miles per hour?

9. If from a sack of flour 32 loaves can be baked each weighing $4\frac{1}{2}$ lb., how many 4-lb. loaves could be baked from a similar sack of flour?

10. Stores in a certain hostel are sufficient to last 56 people for 15 days. If an additional 14 people arrive, how long will the stores now last?

The Ratio Method—Direct

When questions, similar to those with which we have been dealing, involve more than two pairs of quantities which are proportional

to each other, then the Unitary Method may become difficult and clumsy to apply. Hence, after the foregoing brief sketch of this method, we will take up the more widely applicable **Ratio Method.**

From a reconsideration of worked example (5) we will find that the Ratio Method is really an abbreviated development of the Unitary Method.

Example 5. If 13 cwt. of material cost £8 9s., what will 48 cwt. cost?

$$13 \text{ cwt. of material cost }\; £8\ 9s. \quad . \quad . \quad . \quad . \quad (1)$$

$$\therefore 1 \text{ cwt. } \text{,, } \quad \text{,, } \quad \text{cost } \frac{£8\ 9s.}{13} \quad . \quad . \quad . \quad (2)$$

$$\therefore 48 \text{ cwt. } \text{,, } \quad \text{,, } \quad \text{cost } \frac{£8\ 9s.}{13} \times 48 \; . \quad . \quad . \quad (3)$$

Line (3) might be written thus,

$$48 \text{ cwt. of material cost } £8\ 9s. \times \frac{48}{13} = £31\ 4s.$$

The quantity $\frac{48}{13}$ may be referred to as (i) **the multiplying ratio**

or (ii) **the multiplying fraction**

and by using it line (2) may be completely omitted.

Note that this multiplying ratio is obtained from the associated pair of quantities in the information given—in this case the 13 cwt. and the 48 cwt.

But this raises the difficulty as to whether this multiplying ratio should be $\frac{48}{13}$ or $\frac{13}{48}$.

This may be answered quickly in the following way:

$$13 \text{ cwt. of material cost } £8\ 9s.$$
$$\therefore 48 \text{ cwt. } \text{,, } \quad \text{,, } \quad \text{,, } \quad £8\ 9s. \times (\text{multiplying ratio})$$

Will 48 cwt. cost more or less than 13 cwt.?—**More**

$$\therefore \text{ Multiplying ratio is greater than 1 and } = \frac{48}{13}$$

Hence result.

Example 7. Find the price of 2 tons 16 cwt. of coal when 1 ton 4 cwt. cost £9 7s. 6d.

1 ton 4 cwt., i.e. $1\frac{1}{5}$ tons, of coal cost £9 7s. 6d.

∴ 2 tons 16 cwt., i.e. $2\frac{4}{5}$ tons, of coal cost £$9\frac{3}{8} \times \dfrac{2\frac{4}{5}}{1\frac{1}{5}}$

$$= £\dfrac{\overset{25}{\cancel{75}}}{8} \times \dfrac{\overset{7}{\cancel{14}}}{\underset{1}{\cancel{5}}} \times \dfrac{\overset{1}{\cancel{5}}}{\underset{2}{\cancel{6}}}$$

$$= £\dfrac{175}{8}$$

$$= £21 \ 17s. \ 6d.$$

EXERCISE 11D

1. If 3 tons 15 cwt. of coal cost £22, find the price of 6 tons 10 cwt.

2. How much will a man earn in 16 days, if he earns £3 17s. 6d. in 3 days?

3. If 13 lb. of coffee cost £4 11s., how many lb. would be bought for £12 12s.?

4. If £1 19s. 8d. buys 14 articles, how many articles can be bought for £2 8s. 2d.?

5. If 550 yd. of wire netting cost £7 5s., find the cost of $1\frac{1}{2}$ miles of netting.

6. If £3 7s. 6d. can purchase 45 books, how many can be bought for $2\frac{1}{2}$ guineas?

7. If 2 cwt. 1 qr. 20 lb. of tea cost £19 5s. 4d., find the cost of 3 qr. 5 lb.

8. If 7 yd. 1 ft. of cloth cost £5 2s. 8d., what length should be obtained for £3 5s. 4d.?

9. If the carriage of 3 cwt. 2 qr. 14 lb. for a certain distance be £10 3s., what weight can be carried the same distance for £51 12s. 6d.?

10. If 58 bushels of corn cost £18 7s. 4d., how many can be bought for £11 14s. 4d.?

11. If $3\frac{3}{4}$ st. of potatoes cost 3s. $1\frac{1}{2}d.$, what weight of potatoes can be bought for 18s. 4d.?

12. If 3 cwt. 12 lb. of goods cost £13 14s. 6d., find the cost of 5 cwt. 20 lb.

13. If a length of $1\frac{1}{8}$ in. on a map represents an actual distance of 330 yd., how many inches will represent an actual distance of $\frac{1}{4}$ mile?

14. If 3 yd. 1 ft. of cloth cost £1 9s. 2d., find the cost of 13 yd. 2 ft.

15. An owner whose house has a frontage of 7 yd. 2 ft. 4 in. pays £32 13s. 4d. for making a road in front of his house. What would be paid by an owner whose house has a frontage of 11 yd. 2 ft. 6 in.?

The Ratio Method—Inverse

We will repeat worked example (6) on p. 138.

Example 6. If 4 men can do a job in 24 hours, how many men could do it in 16 hours?

$$24 \text{ hr. is time required for job by 4 men} \quad . \quad . \quad . \quad (1)$$
$$\therefore 1 \text{ hr. ,, ,, ,, ,, ,, ,, } 4 \times 24 \text{ men} \quad . \quad . \quad (2)$$
$$\therefore 16 \text{ hr. ,, ,, ,, ,, ,, ,, } 4 \times \frac{24}{16} \text{ men} \quad . \quad . \quad (3)$$
$$= 6 \text{ men}$$

In this case the multiplying ratio is $\frac{24}{16}$, obtained in the following way:

$$24 \text{ hr. is time taken by 4 men}$$
$$\therefore 16 \text{ hr. ,, ,, ,, ,, } 4 \times \text{(multiplying ratio)}$$

Will 16 hr. be required by more or less men than require 24 hr.?—
More

$$\therefore \text{ Multiplying ratio is greater than 1 and } = \frac{24}{16}$$
Hence result.

Note that in this case the time taken is **less** than original.
∴ Number of men required is **more** than original.

Example 8. If 6 men require 3 hr. 5 min. to do a certain piece of work, how long would 10 men require?

$$\text{Time required for 6 men to do job} = 3 \text{ hr. 5 min.}$$
$$= 3\tfrac{1}{12} \text{ hr.}$$
$$\therefore \text{Time required for 10 men to do job} = 3\tfrac{1}{12} \times \tfrac{6}{10} \text{ hr.}$$
$$= \frac{\overset{1}{\cancel{37}}}{\underset{2}{\cancel{12}}} \times \frac{\cancel{6}}{10}$$
$$= 1 \text{ hr. 51 min.}$$

EXERCISE 11E

1. In how many days can 20 men do a piece of work which 125 men can do in 32 days?

2. A certain quantity of hay can feed 60 cows for 1 week. How many cows could the same quantity feed for 28 days?

3. A farmer has enough food to last 30 cattle for 150 days. How long would the same food last 50 cattle?

4. If 25 men take 36 days to do a piece of work, how long will 12 men take?

5. A cyclist whose speed is 12 miles per hour takes 20 minutes to cover a certain distance. How long will it take a cyclist whose rate of travel is 15 miles per hour?

6. If 20 dozen eggs could be bought for a certain sum of money when eggs cost 4s. 6d. per dozen, how many could be bought for the same money when eggs cost 6s. 9d. per dozen?

7. In a coal mine, the winding engine raises the cage in 3 min. 20 sec. when it works at 36 revolutions per minute. If the speed be increased to 40 revolutions per minute, how long will it take to raise the cage?

8. If a person travelling 12 hours a day can perform a journey in 24 days, in how many days could he perform the same journey, supposing he travelled 16 hours a day?

9. A garrison of 638 men has provisions for 240 days. If it be reinforced by 418 men, how long will the provisions now last?

10. On a certain day, a Naval Barracks takes in sufficient provisions to last the garrison of 624 men for 30 days. On the same day a full destroyer crew of 156 is suddenly called away. How long should the provisions last the garrison remaining?

11. A garrison of 5,000 men has provisions for 55 days. After 10 days, 500 men are removed. How long will the provisions now last at the same rate per man?

12. A garrison of 4,000 men has provisions for 128 days, and after 80 days is reinforced by 800 men. How long will the provisions now last at the same rate per man?

The Ratio Method—Several Varying Quantities

In questions involving a number of varying quantities, the Ratio Method should be applied to each pair of such quantities in turn.

Example 9. If 15 men can build a wall 7 ft. long, 15 ft. high,

14 in. thick in 16 days, in how many days will 10 men build a wall 35 ft. long, 14 ft. high and 9 in. thick?

15 men build a wall   7 ft. long, 15 ft. high, 14 in. thick in 16 days
∴ 10 men build a wall 35 ft. long, 14 ft. high,   9 in. thick in

$$16 \times \frac{\overset{8}{\cancel{15}}}{\underset{\underset{1}{2}}{\cancel{10}}} \times \frac{\overset{5}{\cancel{35}}}{\cancel{7}} \times \frac{\overset{1}{\cancel{14}}}{\cancel{15}} \times \frac{\overset{1}{9}}{\cancel{14}} \text{ days}$$

$$= 72 \text{ days}$$

Note that in this question there are **four** distinct multiplying ratios. These ratios are obtained by considering each pair of quantities in turn,

(1) number of men; (2) length of wall; (3) height of wall;
(4) thickness of wall.

Example 10. If 7 tractors mow 111 acres in 3 days, working 8 hours a day, how many tractors could mow a field twice the size in 7 days, working 4 hours longer each day at $\frac{2}{3}$ of the original rate?

Working 3 days of 8 hours at a certain rate 111 acres are mown by 7 tractors

∴ Working 7 days of 12 hours at $\frac{2}{3}$ certain rate 222 acres are mown by

$$7 \times \frac{3}{7} \times \frac{\overset{2}{\cancel{8}}}{\underset{\underset{1}{4}}{\cancel{12}}} \times \frac{3}{2} \times \frac{\overset{2}{\cancel{222}}}{\underset{1}{\cancel{111}}} \text{ tractors}$$

$$= 6 \text{ tractors}$$

EXERCISE 11F

1. If 25 men can do a job in 3 days of 8 hours each, how many hours per day must 24 men work to do the same job in 5 days?

2. If 8 pumps can raise 2,000 tons of water in 8 hours, how many pumps can raise 2,500 tons of water in 20 hours working at the same rate?

3. If 1,500 copies of a book of 352 pages require 66 reams of paper, how many reams will be required for 4,000 copies of a similar book of 396 pages?

4. If 35 tons of coal be carried 24 miles for £3 15s., how many tons will be carried 42 miles for £5 5s.?

5. If the cost of printing 500 booklets of 16 pages be £7 10s., what would be the cost of printing 750 similar booklets of 12 pages?

6. The Customs' duty on 50 packages each weighing 1 cwt. 1 qr. 19 lb. is £33 2s. 6d. Find the duty on 75 packages of similar material each weighing 96 lb.

7. If 17 men earn £115 14s. $1\frac{1}{2}d$. in 11 days, how much will 9 men earn in 21 days at the same rate?

8. If the carriage of 1 cwt. 56 lb. by goods train for 20 miles is 6s. 3d., what would be the cost of carriage of 84 lb. for 64 miles by passenger train if the goods train rate is $\frac{2}{3}$ of that of the passenger train?

9. If 18 pumps can raise 2,150 tons of water in 10 days working 8 hours a day, in how many days could 16 similar pumps raise 1,290 tons of water working 9 hours a day?

10. If 12 fires, burning for 9 hours per day, consume $6\frac{3}{4}$ tons of coal in 25 days, how much coal will be consumed by 30 such fires burning 8 hours a day for 30 days?

11. If 6 st. 1 lb. of flour serve 17 men for 5 days, how long will 17 cwt. serve 8 men and a boy, the boy eating half the quantity a man eats?

12. The charge made for 36 electric lamps burning 8 hours per night during the month of December was £23 6s. 8d. What should be the charge for 120 similar lamps burning 3 hours per night during the months of July and August?

13. When meat was 3s. per lb. it cost £24 to supply 12 persons for 5 weeks. How much will it cost to supply 18 persons for 7 weeks when meat is 4s. per lb.?

14. When petrol cost 3s. 4d. per gallon, a motor car which runs 30 miles to the gallon used petrol costing £1 6s. 8d. on a certain journey. When the price of petrol was increased to 3s. 8d. per gallon, what was the petrol bill for the same journey made by a car which runs 24 miles to the gallon?

15. A contractor undertakes to do a certain job in 12 days. He finds that 195 men working for the first $5\frac{1}{2}$ days overtake only $\frac{3}{8}$ of the work. How many additional men must be engaged in order to complete the work in the scheduled time? Find the wage bill for the completed job if each man is paid 22s. 6d. per day.

Simple Proportional Parts

The four numbers 2, 3, 8, 12 are said to be **in proportion** because

Ratio of 1st two numbers ($\frac{2}{3}$) = Ratio of 2nd two numbers ($\frac{8}{12}$)

This can be generalized for the four numbers a, b, c, d which are in **proportion** if

Ratio of a to b = Ratio of c to d

$$\text{i.e. } \frac{a}{b} = \frac{c}{d}$$

This leads to the possibility of dividing numbers or quantities into parts proportional to other numbers or quantities.

Example 1. Divide a block of chocolate containing 24 'squares' between two people A and B in the ratio 3 : 5, i.e. in parts proportional to the numbers 3 and 5.

Then A's share : B's share = 3 : 5

It is convenient to divide the chocolate into $3 + 5$, i.e. 8 equal parts. Of these equal parts, A receives 3 and B receives 5 as their proper shares. But, the number of 'squares' in each of these equal parts

$$= \frac{\text{total to be divided}}{\text{number of equal parts}} = \frac{24}{8} = 3$$

$$\therefore \text{ A's share} = 3 \text{ equal parts} = 3 \times 3 = 9 \text{ 'squares'}$$
$$\text{B's share} = 5 \text{ equal parts} = 5 \times 3 = 15 \text{ 'squares'}$$

This can be abbreviated in the following way:

$$\text{A's share : B's share} = 3 : 5$$
$$\text{Number of equal parts} = 3 + 5 = 8$$

$$\therefore \text{ A's share} = \overset{3}{\cancel{24}} \times \frac{3}{\underset{1}{8}} = 9 \text{ squares}$$

$$\text{B's share} = \overset{3}{\cancel{24}} \times \frac{5}{\underset{1}{8}} = 15 \text{ squares}$$

$$\text{Total} = \underline{24 \text{ squares}}$$

As a useful check on working it is advisable to add together the shares of each person involved to make sure that the total corresponds to the quantity being divided.

Example 2. Divide a block of chocolate containing 24 'squares' into three parts proportional to the numbers 3, 4 and 5.

$$\text{1st portion : 2nd portion : 3rd portion} = 3 : 4 : 5$$
$$\text{Number of equal parts} = 3 + 4 + 5 = 12$$
$$\text{1st portion} = 24 \times \tfrac{3}{12} = 6 \text{ squares}$$
$$\text{2nd portion} = 24 \times \tfrac{4}{12} = 8 \text{ squares}$$
$$\text{3rd portion} = 24 \times \tfrac{5}{12} = 10 \text{ squares}$$
$$\text{Total} = \underline{24 \text{ squares}}$$

Consider the ratio of the fractions $\tfrac{1}{3} : \tfrac{1}{2}$.

$$\text{This ratio} = \frac{\frac{1}{3}}{\frac{1}{2}} = \tfrac{1}{3} \times \tfrac{2}{1} = \tfrac{2}{3} \quad . \quad . \quad . \quad . \quad \text{(A)}$$

Now the L.C.M. of the denominators of the fractions forming the original ratio $= 6$.

Multiply each term of the original ratio by 6

$$\therefore \text{ Ratio} = \tfrac{1}{3} \times 6 : \tfrac{1}{2} \times 6$$
$$= 2 : 3$$

But, by comparison with (A) we see that the result just obtained is identical with (A). Hence we have this important general result

that a ratio is unaltered by multiplying or dividing each of its terms by the same number.

Example 3. Divide £7 16s. into three parts proportional to $\frac{1}{2}$, $\frac{1}{3}$, $\frac{1}{4}$.

$$\text{1st sum : 2nd sum : 3rd sum} = \tfrac{1}{2} : \tfrac{1}{3} : \tfrac{1}{4}$$
$$= 6 : 4 : 3 \quad \text{(By multiplication by L.C.M. 12)}$$

Number of equal parts $= 6 + 4 + 3 = 13$

$$\therefore \text{1st sum} = £7 \ 16s. \times \tfrac{6}{13} = £\frac{\overset{3}{\cancel{39}}}{\underset{1}{5}} \times \frac{6}{\cancel{13}} = £3 \ 12s.$$

$$\text{2nd sum} = £7 \ 16s. \times \tfrac{4}{13} = £\frac{\overset{3}{\cancel{39}}}{\underset{1}{5}} \times \frac{4}{\cancel{13}} = £2 \ 8s.$$

$$\text{3rd sum} = £7 \ 16s. \times \tfrac{3}{13} = £\frac{\overset{3}{\cancel{39}}}{\underset{1}{5}} \times \frac{3}{\cancel{13}} = £1 \ 16s.$$

$$\text{Total} = £7 \ 16s.$$

EXERCISE 12A

1. A block of chocolate containing 32 'squares' is divided between two children in the ratio of 7 : 9. How many squares does each receive?

2. If 143 wooden bricks are divided between three children in proportion to the numbers 2, 4 and 5, how many bricks does each child receive?

3. Divide £180 into three parts proportional to 4, 5 and 6.

4. Divide £12 13s. between three people, A, B and C, in the ratio of 6 : 7 : 10.

5. Divide £87 13s. into three parts proportional to the numbers 3, 4 and 5.

6. A sum of £822 16s. is to be divided among three communities in proportion to their population. If the populations are 2,430, 3,057 and 684, find the share of each community.

7. Divide £7 7s. into three parts in the proportion of $\frac{1}{4}$, $\frac{2}{5}$ and $\frac{1}{6}$.

8. If 11 tons 14 cwt. of coal is divided between three people in the ratio of $\frac{1}{2} : \frac{1}{3} : \frac{1}{4}$, how much coal does each receive?

9. Divide £53 4s. into three parts proportional to 2, $2\frac{1}{4}$ and $2\frac{2}{5}$.

10. The three ingredients in a cake weighing 11 lb. 4 oz. are in the ratio of $3\cdot3 : 0\cdot7 : 0\cdot5$. What quantities of each ingredient are used?

11. Divide £49 6s. 8d. into four parts proportional to 1, 2, 3 and 4.

12. Gunpowder is composed of nitre, charcoal and sulphur in the proportion of 33, 7 and 5. How many lb. of charcoal are there in 90 lb. of gunpowder? How many lb. of gunpowder will contain 15·4 of nitre?

13. Divide 2 tons 7 cwt. 21 lb. into two parts, one of which is $\frac{2}{5}$ of the other.

14. Divide £21 13s. 4d. between A, B and C, so that A gets $\frac{3}{5}$ of B's share and B and C get equal shares.

15. Divide £31 10s. between A and B so that for every 11s. that A receives, B may receive 3s.

16. Divide £14 6s. 8d. among A, B and C so that for every shilling given to A, B gets 10s. and C a half-guinea.

17. Divide £5 12s. 6d. between A, B, C and D so that for every 6d. A gets, B may get 9d., C may get 1s. and D may get 1s. 6d.

18. Divide £27 19s. into an equal number of half-guineas, crowns, half-crowns, florins, shillings and sixpences.

19. Find the area of a rectangular field whose perimeter is half of a mile and whose breadth is $\frac{3}{8}$ of its length.

20. The sides of a triangle are proportional to 4, 5 and 7; the smallest side is 3 ft. 2 in. Find the perimeter of the triangle.

Example 4. Three men, A, B and C, enter into partnership in a business. A invests capital of £187 10s., B £150 and C £125. If a profit of £129 10s. is divided between them in the ratio of their investments, how much should each receive?

$$\text{A's share : B's share : C's share}$$
$$= £187 \; 10s. : \quad £150 \quad : \quad £125$$
$$= \quad 375 \quad : \quad 300 \quad : \quad 250$$
$$= \quad 15 \quad : \quad 12 \quad : \quad 10$$

No. of equal parts $= 15 + 12 + 10 = 37$

$$\therefore \text{A's share} = £129 \; 10s. \times \tfrac{15}{37} = £\frac{\overset{7}{259}}{2} \times \frac{15}{\underset{1}{37}} = £52 \; 10s.$$

$$\text{B's share} = £129 \ 10s. \times \tfrac{12}{37} = £\frac{\overset{7}{\cancel{259}}}{\underset{1}{\cancel{2}}} \times \frac{\overset{6}{\cancel{12}}}{\underset{1}{\cancel{37}}} = £42$$

$$\text{C's share} = £129 \ 10s. \times \tfrac{10}{37} = £\frac{\overset{7}{\cancel{259}}}{\underset{1}{\cancel{2}}} \times \frac{\overset{5}{\cancel{10}}}{\underset{1}{\cancel{37}}} = £35$$

$$\text{Total} = \underline{\underline{£129 \ 10s.}}$$

Example 5. Divide £8 5s. between three people, A, B and C, so that A gets $\frac{3}{7}$ of B's share and B gets $\frac{2}{5}$ of C's share.

A's share : B's share $\qquad = 3 : 7 \qquad = 6 : 14$

$\qquad$ B's share : C's share $= \ \ 2 : 5 \quad = \quad 14 : 35$

$\therefore$ A's share : B's share : C's share $= 6 : 14 : 35$

$\qquad$ No. of equal parts $= 6 + 14 + 35 = 55$

$$\therefore \text{A's share} = £8 \ 5s. \times \tfrac{6}{55} = £\frac{\overset{3}{\cancel{33}}}{\underset{2}{\cancel{4}}} \times \frac{\overset{3}{\cancel{6}}}{\underset{5}{\cancel{55}}} = \quad 18s.$$

$$\text{B's share} = £8 \ 5s. \times \tfrac{14}{55} = £\frac{\overset{3}{\cancel{33}}}{\underset{2}{\cancel{4}}} \times \frac{\overset{7}{\cancel{14}}}{\underset{5}{\cancel{55}}} = £2 \ 2s.$$

$$\text{C's share} = £8 \ 4s. \times \tfrac{35}{55} = £\frac{\overset{3}{\cancel{33}}}{\underset{2}{\cancel{4}}} \times \frac{\overset{7}{\cancel{35}}}{\underset{\underset{5}{\cancel{5}}}{\cancel{55}}} = £5 \ 5s.$$

$$\text{Total} = \underline{\underline{£8 \ 5s.}}$$

EXERCISE 12B

1. A and B are partners in a business. If A invests £210 and B £270 capital, what share should each get of a profit of £216?

2. A, B and C enter into partnership. A puts in £315, B £225 and C £270. How should a profit of £324 be divided among them?

3. Divide £18 13s. 4d. between three boys, A, B and C, so that A gets twice as much as B and B twice as much as C.

4. Three partners, A, B, C, invest £1,200, £1,500 and £1,900 in

a business. At the end of a year the profits were £345. How should this be divided between them?

5. Divide a profit of £187 10s. between A, B and C, each of whom have invested £162 15s., £186 and £232 10s. respectively in a certain business.

6. Divide £948 10s. between Peter, James and John, so that Peter receives three times as much as John, and John half as much again as James.

7. The cost of roof repairs in a flatted house is £25 10s. It is shared by three tenants in proportion to their assessed rentals which are £62, £60 and £48. What does each tenant pay?

8. A tax of £72,000 is to be raised from three towns, each of which will pay a sum proportional to its assessed rental. The respective rentals of the towns are £107,418, £335,697 and £516,885. Calculate the sum to be paid by each town.

9. Divide £318 3s. among A, B and C, so that A's share may be to B's share as 3 : 5 and B's share to C's share as 10 : 11.

10. A, B and C are partners in a business in which they have invested £3,500, £2,000 and £1,500 respectively. A total profit of £1,050 is divided between them in amounts proportional to the sum each invests. Find the share of the profit each receives.

11. In a certain examination three pupils X, Y, Z score altogether 2,190 marks. X's marks are to Y's marks in the ratio of 4 : 3 and Y's to Z's as 7 : 8. How many marks did each score?

12. Divide £502 5s. among four persons A, B, C and D, so that A may have twice as much as B, B three times as much as C, and C four times as much as D.

13. Two men, A and B, own a business. The profits for a certain year amounted to £1,296. Out of these profits A is given £400 as manager and then the remainder is divided between A and B in the ratio 4 : 3. How much do A and B each receive?

14. A invests £5,000 in a business, B £3,750 and C £4,000. B is paid £450 a year as manager and the remaining profits are shared in proportion to the capital of each. How much does each receive if the year's profit is £3,850?

15. A with £700 joins B with £1,250 in a business and in a year they lose £390 and their capitals are reduced proportionally. Find the capitals with which they start the second year.

C now joins them with £800 and at the end of the second year the profits are £1,227 4s. What share of the profits should each receive if these are divided in proportion to their capitals at the beginning of the year?

13

Percentages

In working with vulgar fractions we have seen that frequently it is useful to be able to express any such fraction with some particular denominator.

For example: $\frac{1}{2}$, $\frac{2}{3}$, $\frac{3}{4}$, $\frac{4}{5}$ can all be expressed with a common denominator 60, thus, $\frac{30}{60}$, $\frac{40}{60}$, $\frac{45}{60}$, $\frac{48}{60}$.

A common denominator widely used is 100, introducing the fraction or ratio known as a **percentage.** The Latin root of this word is 'centum', meaning 'a hundred', and when we talk about 'so much per cent.' we imply a certain ratio with denominator 100. Thus, 35 per cent. $= \frac{35}{100}$.

The symbol '%' is that used to express per cent., so that $35\% = \frac{35}{100}$.

Ability to express quickly any percentage as a fraction and any fraction as a percentage will be valuable to the student

To express a Percentage as a Fraction

Example 1. (A) Express 60% as a fraction in its lowest terms.

$$60\% = \frac{60}{100} = \frac{3}{5}$$

(B) Evaluate 60% of 120.

$$60\% \text{ of } 120 = \frac{6\emptyset}{1\emptyset\emptyset} \times 12\emptyset$$
$$= 72$$

(C) Evaluate 60% of 3 tons.

$$60\% \text{ of } 3 \text{ tons} = \frac{\overset{3}{\cancel{6\emptyset}}}{\underset{5}{\cancel{1\emptyset\emptyset}}} \times 3 \text{ tons}$$
$$= 1 \text{ ton } 16 \text{ cwt.}$$

151

EXERCISE 13A. *Oral*

Express the following percentages as fractions in their lowest terms:

1. 10%	**2.** 20%	**3.** 50%	**4.** 80%	**5.** 5%
6. 15%	**7.** 25%	**8.** 45%	**9.** 75%	**10.** 95%
11. 4%	**12.** 8%	**13.** 16%	**14.** $33\frac{1}{3}$%	**15.** $66\frac{2}{3}$%
16. $16\frac{2}{3}$%	**17.** $2\frac{1}{2}$%	**18.** $12\frac{1}{2}$%	**19.** $37\frac{1}{2}$%	**20.** $62\frac{1}{2}$%
21. $6\frac{1}{4}$%	**22.** $8\frac{1}{3}$%	**23.** $3\frac{1}{3}$%	**24.** $6\frac{2}{3}$%	**25.** $13\frac{1}{3}$%
26. 120%	**27.** 125%	**28.** $133\frac{1}{3}$%	**29.** $112\frac{1}{2}$%	**30.** 135%

Certain percentages of frequent occurrence in everyday life should be memorized in their equivalent fractional form.

Conversion Table

$5\% = \frac{1}{20}$	$10\% = \frac{1}{10}$	$20\% = \frac{1}{5}$	$50\% = \frac{1}{2}$
$25\% = \frac{1}{4}$	$75\% = \frac{3}{4}$	$2\frac{1}{2}\% = \frac{1}{40}$	$12\frac{1}{2}\% = \frac{1}{8}$
$37\frac{1}{2}\% = \frac{3}{8}$	$62\frac{1}{2}\% = \frac{5}{8}$	$87\frac{1}{2}\% = \frac{7}{8}$	$33\frac{1}{3}\% = \frac{1}{3}$
$66\frac{2}{3}\% = \frac{2}{3}$	$16\frac{2}{3}\% = \frac{1}{6}$	$8\frac{1}{3}\% = \frac{1}{12}$	$3\frac{1}{3}\% = \frac{1}{30}$
$6\frac{2}{3}\% = \frac{1}{15}$	$6\frac{1}{4}\% = \frac{1}{16}$	$112\frac{1}{2}\% = 1\frac{1}{8}$	$125\% = 1\frac{1}{4}$
	$133\frac{1}{3}\% = 1\frac{1}{3}$	$166\frac{2}{3}\% = 1\frac{2}{3}$	

EXERCISE 13B

Express the following percentages as fractions in their lowest terms:

1. 6%	**2.** 12%	**3.** 18%	**4.** 64%	**5.** 84%
6. 36%	**7.** 68%	**8.** 72%	**9.** $27\frac{1}{2}$%	**10.** $36\frac{2}{3}$%
11. 140%	**12.** $102\frac{1}{2}$%	**13.** $116\frac{2}{3}$%	**14.** $162\frac{1}{2}$%	**15.** $105\frac{1}{4}$%
16. $13\frac{3}{4}$%	**17.** $5\frac{5}{9}$%	**18.** $4\frac{6}{11}$%	**19.** $14\frac{2}{7}$%	**20.** $7\frac{9}{13}$%

Find the value of:

21. 3% of 150	**22.** 4% of 750
23. $6\frac{2}{3}$% of 450	**24.** $37\frac{1}{2}$% of 64
25. $107\frac{1}{2}$% of 144	**26.** $123\frac{1}{3}$% of 720
27. $7\frac{1}{2}$% of £90	**28.** $13\frac{1}{3}$% of £66
29. $48\frac{4}{7}$% of £63	**30.** $67\frac{7}{9}$% of £72
31. $134\frac{2}{7}$% of £8 15s.	**32.** $113\frac{3}{4}$% of £6 13s. 4d.
33. $2\frac{1}{2}$% of 3 lb. 2 oz.	**34.** $3\frac{3}{4}$% of 3 tons 10 cwt.

35. $8\frac{1}{3}\%$ of 6 tons 12 cwt.   **36.** $26\frac{1}{4}\%$ of 2 st. 7 lb.

37. $112\frac{1}{2}\%$ of 4 tons 8 cwt.   **38.** $105\frac{5}{9}\%$ of 3 cwt. 96 lb.

39. $3\frac{1}{3}\%$ of 45 yd.   **40.** $7\frac{1}{2}\%$ of $7\frac{1}{2}$ ml.

41. $16\frac{1}{4}\%$ of 8 yd. 2 ft. 8 in.   **42.** $104\frac{6}{11}\%$ of 2 ml. 1,320 yd.

43. $57\frac{1}{7}\%$ of 2 hr. 6 min.   **44.** $13\frac{1}{3}\%$ of 15 acres

45. $122\frac{2}{9}\%$ of 2 cub. ft. 864 cub. in.

To express a Fraction as a Percentage

This is the reverse operation to that which we have been discussing, and the table on p. 152 should be examined again carefully from this point of view.

Example 2. Express the fraction $\frac{4}{5}$ as a percentage.

(A) $\text{Fraction} = \frac{4}{5} = \frac{4 \times 20}{5 \times 20} = \frac{80}{100} = 80\%$

(B) $\text{Fraction} = \frac{4}{5} = \frac{4 \times \frac{100}{5}}{5 \times \frac{100}{5}} = \frac{4 \times 20}{100} = 80\%$

(C) $\text{Fraction} = \frac{4}{5} = \frac{\frac{4}{5} \times 100}{100} = (\frac{4}{5} \times 100) \text{ per } 100 = 80\%$

Essentially the method is that of changing the denominator of the given fraction to 100, and this is only permissible if the numerator is multiplied by the same quantity—(A).

In actual practice the method followed is (C), where the fraction is multiplied by 100 and the result called a percentage (equivalent to dividing by 100).

Example 3. Express the fraction $\frac{13}{16}$ as a percentage.

$$\text{Fraction} = \frac{13}{16} = \frac{13}{\underset{4}{\cancel{16}}} \times \overset{25}{\cancel{100}} \text{ per cent.}^{*}$$

$$= \frac{325}{4}\%$$

$$= 81\frac{1}{4}\%$$

* *Note* that multiplication by 100 per cent. is equivalent to multiplication by $\frac{100}{100}$, i.e. 1.

Example 4. Express the mixed number $2\frac{2}{3}$ as a percentage.

$$\text{Mixed number} = 2\frac{2}{3} = \frac{8}{3} = \frac{8}{3} \times 100 \text{ per cent.}$$

$$= 266\frac{2}{3}\%$$

This question may be done mentally by dividing the mixed number into two parts.

$$\text{Thus } 2\frac{2}{3} = 2 + \frac{2}{3}$$
$$= 200\% + 66\frac{2}{3}\%$$
$$= 266\frac{2}{3}\%$$

Exercise 13c

Express the following fractions and mixed numbers as percentages in their simplest form:

1. $\frac{3}{4}$	**2.** $\frac{4}{5}$	**3.** $\frac{5}{6}$	**4.** $\frac{7}{8}$	**5.** $\frac{11}{12}$
6. $\frac{7}{16}$	**7.** $\frac{13}{20}$	**8.** $\frac{17}{24}$	**9.** $\frac{19}{25}$	**10.** $\frac{31}{40}$
11. $\frac{29}{50}$	**12.** $\frac{17}{32}$	**13.** $\frac{25}{36}$	**14.** $\frac{37}{45}$	**15.** $\frac{43}{60}$
16. $\frac{17}{18}$	**17.** $\frac{53}{84}$	**18.** $\frac{79}{120}$	**19.** $\frac{107}{144}$	**20.** $\frac{127}{150}$
21. $1\frac{2}{5}$	**22.** $2\frac{3}{8}$	**23.** $3\frac{1}{6}$	**24.** $2\frac{7}{12}$	**25.** $4\frac{17}{20}$
26. $5\frac{2}{3}$	**27.** $1\frac{1}{4}$	**28.** $7\frac{11}{15}$	**29.** $6\frac{17}{25}$	**30.** $8\frac{23}{30}$

To express a Quantity as a Percentage of a Similar Quantity.

This is normally done in **two** stages:

    (1) Express one quantity as a ratio of the other quantity.
    (2) Convert the ratio to a percentage.

Example 5. What percentage is 128 of 160?

$$\text{Ratio} = \frac{128}{160} = \frac{4}{5}$$

$$\therefore \text{ Percentage} = \frac{4}{5} \times 100 = 80$$

Example 6. What percentage is 2 yd. 6 in. of 3 yd. 1 ft.?

$$\text{Ratio} = \frac{2 \text{ yd. 6 in.}}{3 \text{ yd. 1 ft.}} = \frac{2\frac{1}{6} \text{ yd.}}{3\frac{1}{3} \text{ yd.}} = \frac{13 \times 3}{6 \times 10} = \frac{13}{20}$$

$$\therefore \text{ Percentage} = \frac{13}{20} \times 100 = 65$$

Example 7. What percentage is 4 tons 15 cwt. of 3 tons 16 cwt.?

$$\text{Ratio} = \frac{4 \text{ tons } 15 \text{ cwt.}}{3 \text{ tons } 16 \text{ cwt.}} = \frac{4\frac{3}{4} \text{ tons}}{3\frac{4}{5} \text{ tons}} = \frac{19 \times 5}{4 \times 19} = \frac{5}{4}$$

$\therefore$ Percentage $= \frac{5}{4} \times 100 = 125$

EXERCISE 13D

Calculate what percentage each of the following quantities is of the other.

1. 24 of 36
2. 96 of 128
3. 28 of 35
4. 45 of 54
5. 5*s.* 1*d.* of 15*s.* 3*d.*
6. 4*s.* 8*d.* of 7*s.* 7*d.*
7. £1 16*s.* of £2 14*s.*
8. £16 5*s.* of £8 9*s.*
9. £3 17*s.* 6*d.* of £5
10. 2*s.* 7½*d.* of £1 13*s.*
11. 5 cwt. of 2 tons
12. 13 cwt. of 1 ton 5 cwt.
13. 15 oz. of 2 lb. 8 oz.
14. 3 cwt. 3 qr. of 2 cwt. 56 lb.
15. 1 cwt. 3 qr. of 5 cwt. 2 qr. 14 lb.
16. 4 tons 5 cwt. 1 qr. of 5 tons 10 cwt.
17. 1 ft. 6 in. of 2 yd.
18. 1 ft. 6 in. of 1 yd. 1 ft. 6 in.
19. 1 ml. 220 yd. of 3 ml. 4 fur.
20. 1 ml. 154 yd. of 1 ml. 6 fur.
21. 3 wk. 1 day of 1 wk. 1 day
22. 2 sq. ft. 14 sq. in. of 3 sq. ft. 68 sq. in
23. 107 sq. yd. 5 sq. ft. of ¼ acre
24. 5 m. 4 dm. 3 cm. of 7 m. 5 dm.
25. 8 cub. ft. 432 cub. in. of 3 cub. yd. 9 cub. ft.

Example 8. If 4*s.* 9*d.* is 12% of a certain sum, find the sum.

$$12\% \text{ of sum} = 4s. \ 9d.$$

i.e. $\frac{12}{100}$ of sum $= 4s. \ 9d.$

$\therefore \frac{100}{100}$ of sum $= 4s. \ 9d \times \dfrac{100}{12}$

$$\therefore \text{Sum} = \frac{\overset{19}{\cancel{57}} \times \overset{25}{\cancel{100}}}{\underset{\underset{1}{3}}{\cancel{12}}} d.$$

$$= 475d.$$
$$= £1 \ 19s. \ 7d.$$

Example 9. If 3 lb. 14 oz. is 31% of a certain weight, find this weight.

$$31\% \text{ of weight} = 3 \text{ lb. 14 oz.}$$

$$\text{i.e. } \tfrac{31}{100} \text{ of weight} = 3\tfrac{7}{8} \text{ lb.}$$

$$\therefore \text{ Weight} = \frac{\overset{1}{\cancel{31}}}{\underset{2}{\cancel{8}}} \times \frac{\overset{25}{\cancel{100}}}{\underset{1}{\cancel{31}}} \text{ lb.}$$

$$= 12\tfrac{1}{2} \text{ lb.}$$

EXERCISE 13E

Find the number of which:

1. 18 is 30%   2. 32 is 48%   3. 72 is 54%
4. 52 is $7\tfrac{1}{7}$%   5. $16\tfrac{1}{4}$ is $12\tfrac{1}{2}$%   6. $21\tfrac{5}{6}$ is $16\tfrac{2}{3}$%
7. 114 is $105\tfrac{5}{9}$%   8. $17\tfrac{3}{5}$ is 110%   9. $24\tfrac{1}{3}$ is $133\tfrac{1}{3}$%

Find the sum of which:

10. £1 10s. is 4%   11. 4s. 6d. is 3%   12. 2s. 6d. is $6\tfrac{2}{3}$%
13. £2 16s. is $37\tfrac{1}{2}$%   14. 6s. 9d. is $7\tfrac{1}{2}$%   15. £8 16s. is $13\tfrac{1}{3}$%
16. 7s. 7d. is $113\tfrac{3}{4}$%   17. £12 is $102\tfrac{6}{7}$%
18. £154 16s. is $107\tfrac{1}{2}$%

Find the weight of which:

19. 3 oz. is $2\tfrac{1}{2}$%   20. 2 cwt. 5 st. is $3\tfrac{3}{4}$%
21. 11 cwt. is $8\tfrac{1}{3}$%   22. 5 lb. 11 oz. is $26\tfrac{1}{4}$%
23. 4 tons 19 cwt. is $112\tfrac{1}{2}$%   24. 4 cwt. 8 lb. is $105\tfrac{5}{9}$%

Find the quantity of which:

25. 1 yd. 1 ft. 6 in. is $3\tfrac{1}{3}$%   26. 4 ft. 4 in. is $16\tfrac{1}{4}$%
27. 4 fur. 110 yd. is $7\tfrac{1}{2}$%   28. 1 hr. 12 min. is $57\tfrac{1}{7}$%
29. 2 ml. 7 fur. is $104\tfrac{6}{11}$%   30. 3 cub. ft. 96 cub. in. is $122\tfrac{2}{9}$%

Miscellaneous Examples

Example 10. A man loses £9 out of a purse containing £45. What percentage of his money does he lose?

$$\text{Original Sum} = £45$$
$$\text{Sum Lost} = £9$$
$$\therefore \text{Fractional Loss} = \frac{£9}{£45} = \tfrac{1}{5}$$
$$\therefore \text{Percentage Loss} = \tfrac{1}{5} \times 100 = 20 \text{ %}$$

Example 11. The boys in a class number 25 and the number of girls is $37\tfrac{1}{2}\%$ of the whole class. What does the whole class number?

$$37\tfrac{1}{2}\% \text{ of whole class are girls}$$
$$\therefore 62\tfrac{1}{2}\% \text{ of whole class are boys}$$
$$\text{i.e. } 62\tfrac{1}{2}\% \text{ of whole class} = 25$$
$$\therefore 100\% \text{ of whole class} = 25 \times \frac{100}{62\tfrac{1}{2}}$$
$$= 25 \times \frac{\overset{40}{\overset{200}{\cancel{200}}}}{\underset{5}{\cancel{125}}}$$
$$\therefore \text{Number in class} = 40$$

Example 12. A man's salary was £800, but was reduced by $7\tfrac{1}{2}\%$. In addition he had to pay 5% of the money he received for superannuation. If he received his salary in 12 equal instalments, what did each instalment amount to?

$$\text{Original Gross Salary} = £800$$
$$\text{Reduction in Salary} = 7\tfrac{1}{2}\% \text{ of } £800 = £60$$
$$\therefore \text{New Gross Salary} = £740$$
$$\text{Amount paid in Superannuation} = 5\% \text{ of } £740 = £37$$
$$\therefore \text{Net Salary} = £703$$
$$\therefore \text{Amount in each monthly instalment} = £\tfrac{703}{12}$$
$$= £58 \; 11s. \; 8d.$$

EXERCISE 13F

1. If $7\frac{1}{2}\%$ of a man's salary is £81, find his salary.

2. A man's income is £480. He pays $7\frac{1}{2}\%$ in taxes and in addition gives 2% to charity. What sum has he left?

3. A box containing 625 oranges was broken and 32% of its contents lost. How many oranges were left in the box?

4. A man spends 92% of his income and saves £92. What is his income?

5. A train which runs at 45 miles per hour is to be speeded up by $16\frac{2}{3}\%$. How far will it then run in 1 hour?

6. The population in a small town on January 1, 1956, was 5,000, and on January 1, 1957, was 5,250. What was the increase per cent. in a year? If the population increases at twice the rate throughout 1957, what should the population be on January 1, 1958?

7. I pay a debt in equal instalments each of $12\frac{1}{2}\%$ of the debt. How many payments do I make before the debt is fully paid? If each instalment is £13 12s. 6d., what is the total debt?

8. On a cross-Channel voyage to this country a ship loses 21 of the cattle which form its cargo. If this is $3\frac{3}{4}\%$ of the number of cattle, how many cattle were landed here?

9. A man's annual salary is increased from £842 to £947 5s. What is the percentage increase in salary?

10. The population of a town is 16,000; if it increases by $7\frac{1}{2}\%$ every year, what will the population be in 2 years?

11. In a forest, 5% of the trees are blown down in a gale, and after 3% of those remaining have been cut down there are still 55,290 standing. How many trees were there in the forest before the gale occurred?

12. In an examination, 60% of the candidates passed, and of those who passed 10% obtained distinction. If 81 of the candidates passed without distinction, how many failed in the examination?

13. In a school of 800 pupils, 45% are girls. 20% of the girls and 10% of the boys failed in Arithmetic at the examination. How many pupils passed in Arithmetic? What percentage of the school passed?

14. At an examination consisting of three subjects there were 400 candidates. Of these, 15% passed in all subjects, 20% in two subjects, and 25% in one subject. How many failed in all three subjects?

15. A rectangle is 12 ft. long and 4 ft. 6 in. broad. If its length is increased by $16\frac{2}{3}\%$ and its breadth by $33\frac{1}{3}\%$, find its increased area. What is the percentage increase in area?

16. A solution of salt contains 24% by weight of salt. If 175 gm. of the solution are diluted with 75 gm. of water, calculate the percentage by weight of salt in the new solution.

17. Of an alloy of copper and zinc, 65% is zinc. 275 lb. of alloy are melted with 50 lb. of pure copper. Find the percentage of copper in the new alloy.

18. A firm's expenses are made up as follows: Rent and Rates, $13\frac{1}{2}$%; New Machinery, $8\frac{1}{2}$%; Wages, 62%; Sundries, 16%. If the amount spent as Sundries was £864, find the amount spent on

(i) Rent and Rates; (ii) Wages

19. A workman earned £10 per week and found that after paying all expenses he could save £1 5s. He removed to a district where he earns 30% more, but his expenses have risen by 35%. How much can he now save in a week?

20. A piece of a certain alloy is found on analysis to consist of the following:

| Aluminium | 3 lb. 8·82 oz. | Manganese | 0·36 oz. |
| Copper | 2·52 oz. | Magnesium | 0·30 oz. |

Find the percentage of each metal in the alloy.

14

Profit and Loss

In the commercial world most transactions are carried through on this principle of **profit and loss**.

When an article is sold for more than it cost, then a **profit** is made

i.e. Selling Price = Cost Price + Profit

When an article is sold for less than it cost, then a **loss** is sustained

i.e. Selling Price = Cost Price − Loss

Sometimes Buying Price is used instead of Cost Price and the following abbreviations may be encountered:

C.P. = Cost Price
B.P. = Buying Price
S.P. = Selling Price

I. Buying and Selling

Example 1. A grocer buys 3 cwt. of tea at £33 6s. 8d. per cwt. and sells it at 6s. 8d. per lb. Find his profit.

Cost Price of 3 cwt. of tea = £100
Selling Price of 1 lb. of tea = 6s. 8d. = £$\frac{1}{3}$
∴ Selling Price of 3 cwt. of tea = £$\frac{1}{3}$ × 336
= £112
∴ Profit on sale = £12

Example 2. A farmer bought 500 sheep at £3 10s. each. He fed them for 3 months at a cost of 4s. 2d. each per month and then sold them at £4 each. Find his total loss.

Sum spent in buying sheep = £3 10s. × 500   = £1,750
Sum spent in feeding sheep = (4s. 2d. × 3) × 500 = £312 10s.

$\therefore$ Total Cost Price of sheep = £2,062 10s.

Total Selling Price of sheep = £4 × 500 = £2,000

$\therefore$ Loss on Transaction = £62 10s.

EXERCISE 14A

1. A grocer buys $2\frac{1}{2}$ cwt. of tea at £35 per cwt. and he sells it at 6s. 10d. per lb. Find his profit.

2. A stationer buys 10 gross of pencils at £1 16s. per gross and sells them at $4\frac{1}{2}d$. each. Find his profit.

3. A man bought a consignment of 64 dozen eggs at 5s. $10\frac{1}{2}d$. per dozen. If 4 dozen are broken in transit and the rest are sold at 6s. per dozen, what loss does he sustain?

4. A dealer buys 20 horses for £1,100 and sells 15 of them at 66 guineas each. At what price must he sell each of the others so as to gain £600?

5. A grocer buys 5 cwt. of sugar at £2 0s. 4d. per cwt. He sells 2 cwt. at $4\frac{1}{2}d$. per lb. and 2 cwt. at $5\frac{1}{2}d$. per lb. At what price per lb. must he sell the rest so as to have neither a profit nor a loss?

6. A farmer bought 100 sheep at £90 per score. He kept them for 10 weeks at a cost of 1s. each per week. At what price per sheep does he sell them if he loses £20?

7. A man bought goods for £45 and sells $\frac{1}{3}$ of them losing $\frac{1}{10}$ of their cost. At what price should he sell the remainder so as to make a profit of £9 on the whole transaction?

8. A merchant bought 1 cwt. of tea at 5s. 8d. per lb. and 2 cwt. at 6s. 4d. per lb. If he mixed the two together, at what price per lb. must he sell the mixture to gain £9 6s. 8d.?

9. A street vendor buys 10 boxes of apples each containing $1\frac{1}{2}$ cwt. at 1s. 2d. per lb. If in each box 10 apples are bad, and the remainder he sells at 4d. each, find his profit. (Reckon 4 apples to 1 lb.)

10. A man buys 90 score of articles at 5 for 4d. and sells them at 4 for 5d.; and another 90 score at 9 for 10d., selling them at 1s. 4d. per dozen. Which is the more profitable transaction and by how much?

11. A man sells an article at 6s. and thereby gains $\frac{1}{5}$ of what it cost him. At what price must he sell it so as to gain $\frac{1}{4}$ of what it cost him?

12. A farmer sold a horse for £80 gaining $\frac{1}{4}$ of what it cost him. If he had lost $\frac{1}{4}$ of the cost price, at what price would he have sold it?

II. Profit and Loss Per Cent. *Same Quantity*

In most business transactions there is a profit or loss involved. It is convenient to express this profit or loss as a **fraction of the cost price** leading to (i) **the fractional profit or loss,** and when this is expressed as a percentage then we get (ii) **the percentage profit or loss.**

This will become clear by considering the following examples.

Example 3. An article which cost £80 is sold for £100. What is the profit per cent.?

$$\text{Cost Price of article} = £80$$

$$\text{Selling Price of article} = £100$$

$$\therefore \text{ Profit on article} = £20$$

$$\therefore \text{ Fractional Profit on article} = \frac{£20}{£80} = \tfrac{1}{4}$$

$$\therefore \text{ Percentage Profit on article} = \tfrac{1}{4} \times 100 = 25$$

Example 4. An article bought for £166 13*s.* 4*d.* is sold for £150. What is the loss per cent.?

$$\text{Cost Price of article} = £166 \text{ } 13s. \text{ } 4d. = £166\tfrac{2}{3}$$

$$\text{Selling Price of article} = £150$$

$$\therefore \text{ Loss on article} = £16\tfrac{2}{3}$$

$$\therefore \text{ Fractional Loss on article} = \frac{£16\tfrac{2}{3}}{£166\tfrac{2}{3}} = \frac{50 \times 3}{3 \times 500} = \tfrac{1}{10}$$

$$\therefore \text{ Percentage Loss on article} = 10$$

Example 5. A horse is sold for £140 at a profit of £15. What is the profit per cent.?

$$\text{Selling Price of horse} = £140$$

$$\text{Profit on horse} = £15$$

$$\therefore \text{ Cost Price of horse} = £125$$

$$\therefore \text{ Fractional Profit on horse} = \frac{£15}{£125} = \tfrac{3}{25}$$

$$\therefore \text{ Percentage Profit on horse} = 12$$

11. By selling an article ... important point 4 on his out-
lay. What loss per cent. ... [faded text]
12. A shopkeeper ... items at 15s. per dozen and sells
...

EXERCISE 14B

Complete the items in the following table:

	Cost Price	Selling Price	Profit (+) or Loss (−)	Fractional Profit/Loss	Percentage Profit/Loss
1.	£8		+£2		
2.	£15	£17 10s.			
3.		£9	+£2 5s.		
4.	£13 6s. 8d.				+10
5.		£7 15s.	−£1 5s.		
6.	£4 3s. 4d.	£3 10s.			
7.	£6 5s.		−8s. 4d.		
8.	£13 10s.				−16⅔
9.			£1 17s. 6d.	+$\frac{1}{8}$	
10.	£4 16s.			−$\frac{1}{12}$	
11.		£10		−$\frac{1}{6}$	
12.		£5 5s.		+$\frac{1}{4}$	

EXERCISE 14C

Calculate the profit or loss per cent. in the following cases:

	Cost Price	Selling Price
1.	£4 10s.	£4 17s. 6d.
2.	£12 5s.	£13 9s. 6d.
3.	£7 13s. 4d.	£6 4s. 7d.
4.	£5 3s. 4d.	£7 15s.
5.	£7 12s. 6d.	£6 2s.
6.	£3 3s.	£2 16s.
7.	£12 16s. 8d.	£14 13s. 4d.

8. A plant which cost 7s. 6d. is sold at 9s. What is the profit per cent.?

9. A book which cost 25s. to produce is sold, during a sale period, for 22s. 6d. What is the loss per cent.?

10. An article bought for £1 15s. is sold for 2 guineas. What is the profit per cent.?

11. By selling an article for 22*s*. 6*d*. a merchant gains $\frac{1}{2}$ on his out-lay. What loss per cent. would he have sustained had he sold it at 13*s*. 9*d*.?

12. A shopkeeper buys 120 balloons at 10*d*. per dozen and sells them at 5 for $4\frac{1}{2}d$. What is his profit per cent.?

III. Profit and Loss Per Cent. *Different Quantities*

Normally merchants, shopkeepers, etc., buy their goods in bulk quantities and sell them to the customer in very small quantities. Thus, sugar may be bought in hundredweights, or even tons, and sold in pounds; tinned foods may be bought in boxes containing 1 gross and sold singly, etc.

In dealing with questions of this type it is essential that we reduce our Cost Price and Selling Price to be that of the **same quantity.**

Example 6. A grocer bought 1 cwt. of tea for £33 12*s*. and sold it at 6*s*. 8*d*. per lb. Find his actual profit and his profit per cent.

$$\text{Cost Price of 1 cwt. of tea} = £33 \ 12s.$$
$$\text{Selling Price of 1 lb. of tea} = 6s. \ 8d.$$
$$\therefore \text{ Selling Price of 1 cwt. of tea} = 6s. \ 8d. \times 112$$
$$= £37 \ 6s. \ 8d.$$
$$\therefore \text{ Profit on 1 cwt. of tea} = £3 \ 14s. \ 8d.$$

$$\therefore \text{ Fractional Profit} = \frac{£3 \ 14s. \ 8d.}{£33 \ 12s.}$$

$$= \frac{3\frac{11}{15}}{33\frac{3}{5}}$$

$$= \frac{\overset{1}{\cancel{56}} \times \overset{1}{\cancel{5}}}{\underset{3}{\cancel{15}} \times \underset{3}{\cancel{168}}}$$

$$= \tfrac{1}{9}$$

$$\therefore \text{ Percentage Profit} = 11\tfrac{1}{9}$$

Example 7. Small toys are bought in bulk at 3 for 10*d*. and sold at 4 for 1*s*. 3*d*. Find the profit per cent.

$$\text{(A)} \qquad \text{Cost Price of 3 toys} = 10d.$$
$$\therefore \text{ Cost Price of 1 toy} = 3\tfrac{1}{3}d.$$
$$\text{Selling Price of 4 toys} = 1s. \ 3d.$$

∴ Selling Price of 1 toy $= 3\frac{3}{4}d.$

∴ Profit on 1 toy $= (3\frac{3}{4}d. - 3\frac{1}{3}d.) = \frac{5}{12}d.$

∴ Fractional Profit $= \dfrac{\frac{5}{12}}{3\frac{1}{3}} = \dfrac{\overset{1}{\cancel{5}}}{\underset{4}{\cancel{12}}} \times \dfrac{\overset{1}{\cancel{3}}}{\underset{2}{\cancel{10}}} = \dfrac{1}{8}$

∴ Percentage Profit $= 12\frac{1}{2}$

or (B) It is probably easier and avoids the introduction of troublesome fractions to consider that a certain number of toys are bought. This 'certain number', in this case, is obtained by finding the L.C.M. of 3 and 4, namely, 12.

Thus,   Cost Price of 3 toys $= 10d.$

∴ Cost Price of 12 toys $= 3s.\ 4d.$

Selling Price of 4 toys $= 1s.\ 3d.$

∴ Selling Price of 12 toys $= 3s.\ 9d.$

∴ Profit on 12 toys $= 5d.$

∴ Fractional Profit $= \dfrac{5d.}{3s.\ 4d.} = \dfrac{5}{40} = \dfrac{1}{8}$

∴ Percentage Profit $= 12\frac{1}{2}$

EXERCISE 14D

Find the percentage profit or loss in the following cases:

Cost Price	Selling Price
1. $4\frac{1}{2}d.$ per lb.	£2 11s. per cwt.
2. £3 3s. per cwt.	6d. per lb.
3. 1s. 9d. per yd.	£23 2s. per furlong
4. £18 per sq. ft.	2s. 4d. per sq. in.
5. £1 6s. 8d. per cub. ft.	£32 per cub. yd.
6. 3s. 4d. per dozen	$3\frac{1}{2}d.$ each
7. 4s. 8d. per dozen	£3 6s. 6d. per gross
8. 1s. 3d. per dozen	1s. 11d. per score
9. 6 for 5d.	5 for 6d.
10. 11 for 1s.	12 for 11d.

11. A grocer buys 1 cwt. of tea for £32 and sells it at 3s. 4d. per $\frac{1}{2}$ lb. packet. Find his actual profit and his profit per cent.

12. A merchant bought 1 ton of sugar at £3 per cwt. and sold it at $7\frac{1}{2}d$. per lb. Find the actual profit made and the profit per cent.

13. A man buys goods wholesale at £12 per cwt. and retails them at 3s. 4d. per lb. If, on an average, $\frac{1}{20}$ of every consignment he receives is damaged and unsaleable, but all the rest is sold, what percentage profit does he make?

14. 300 oranges are bought for £6. $2\frac{1}{2}$ doz. of the oranges are unfit for sale. The remaining oranges are sold at 5s. per dozen. Find the gain or loss per cent.

15. A merchant buys 3 cwt. of tea at £26 13s. 4d. per cwt. and 2 cwt. at £22 10s. per cwt. He mixes the two lots and sells the mixture at 6s. 3d. per lb. Find his actual gain and his percentage gain on the whole transaction.

16. Half-a-gross of tennis racquets were bought at 50s. each. A sufficient number were sold at 72s. each to recover the amount of this outlay. The remainder were sold at cost price. Find (i) the total gain; (ii) the gain per cent.

17. Raw material is bought for £62 10s. per ton and manufacturing costs amount to £2 9s. 6d. per cwt. If the finished product is sold at 1s. 2d. per lb., find the profit per cent.

18. A man buys $14\frac{2}{3}$ dozen articles for £1 0s. 3d. and sells them at 11 for 1s. $1\frac{1}{2}d$. Find (i) his loss per cent.; (ii) how many articles must be sold to give a loss of 9s.

19. A coal merchant buys 2 trucks each containing 8 tons of coal at £50 per truck. He sold 12 tons at 7s. 8d. per cwt. and the remainder at 7s. 4d. per cwt. What was his total profit and his profit per cent.?

20. The cost of printing 1,000 magazines was $8\frac{1}{4}d$. per copy. Of these, 50 were given away free, 750 were sold at 1s. each and the rest were sold off at 9d. per copy. Find (i) how much profit was made on the whole issue; (ii) what percentage of the total cost this profit represents.

15

Simple Interest

Most people are familiar in a general way with the main terms of banking, whether this has been acquired through contact with the Post Office Savings Bank, local City Savings Banks, or with some national bank such as Martin's, British Linen, etc.

Let us revise these terms:

1. **Principal**—the sum of money invested is known as the Principal.

2. **Interest**—the sum of money obtained for the use of invested money is called the Interest.

3. **Time**—the number of years for which the sum is invested is the Time.

4. **Rate Per Cent.**—the sum of money obtained for the use of **each** £100 for **one** year is called the 'rate per cent. per annum'.

5. **Amount**—When a sum of money is invested for a given time at a given rate, then interest accrues. The sum invested plus the interest accruing is known as the Amount.

Hence,

Amount = Principal + Interest

It should be clearly understood that when a person invests money in a bank, then interest is paid to the investor for the use of his money. Similarly, when a person borrows money from the bank, then he pays interest to the bank for the privilege of using its money.

There are several other important points to which close attention should be given.

1. Time should always be reckoned in years and/or fractions of a year.

2. In reckoning the time between two dates, only one of the stated days should be included.

e.g. Find the number of days between January 15th, 1955, and July 7th, 1955.

Number of days between January 15th, 1955, and July 7th, 1955

$= (31-15)$ January $+28$ February $+31$ March $+30$ April $+31$ May
$+30$ June $+7$ July

$= (16+28+31+30+31+30+7)$

$= 173$

3. Care should be taken in reckoning days in the February month of a 'leap' year.

4. A rate of 5% per annum means that the interest on £100 invested for 1 year is £5.

There are two kinds of interest: (i) **Simple Interest**;
(ii) **Compound Interest.**

In **Simple Interest,** the interest for two years is twice that for one year, the interest for three years is thrice that for one year, etc.

i.e. Simple Interest is proportional to the time of investment and is always used when a sum of money is invested for only part of a year.

In **Compound Interest,** the interest is added to the principal at the end of each year and hence this interest itself acquires interest in subsequent years.

We are concerned here with Simple Interest.

In this treatment of our subject we will find that all of the examples can be solved by use of the Ratio Method. The reason for this is that the Simple Interest accruing is directly proportional to the Principal and the Rate as well as the Time.

Thus, if the Principal is doubled, then the Interest is doubled;
if the Time is trebled, then the Interest is trebled;
if the Rate is halved, then the Interest is halved, etc.

To find Simple Interest (I)

Example 1. Find the Simple Interest on £175 for 3 years at 4% per annum.

Interest on £100 for 1 year $= £4$

$\therefore$ Interest on £175 for 3 years $= £4 \times \dfrac{\overset{7}{\cancel{175}}}{\underset{1}{\cancel{100}}} \times \dfrac{3}{\underset{1}{1}}$

$\underset{1}{\overset{25}{}}$

$= £21$

Example 2. Find the Simple Interest on £725 for 1 year 146 days at $5\frac{1}{3}$% per annum.

$$1 \text{ year } 146 \text{ days} = 1\tfrac{2}{5} \text{ years}$$

$$\text{Interest on £100 for 1 year} = £5\tfrac{1}{3}$$

$$\therefore \text{ Interest on £725 for } 1\tfrac{2}{5} \text{ years} = £\frac{16}{3} \times \frac{\overset{\overset{29}{\cancel{145}}}{\cancel{725}}}{\underset{\underset{5}{\cancel{25}}}{\cancel{100}}} \times \frac{7}{\underset{1}{\cancel{5}}}$$

$$= £\frac{812}{15}$$

$$= £54 \text{ } 2s. \text{ } 8d.$$

EXERCISE 15A

Find the Simple Interest on:

1. £450 in 2 years at 4% per annum.
2. £325 in 3 years at 5% per annum.
3. £625 in 4 years at $4\frac{1}{2}$% per annum.
4. £280 in $7\frac{1}{2}$ years at 7% per annum.
5. £981 in $3\frac{1}{3}$ years at $5\frac{1}{2}$% per annum.
6. £738 in 6 yr. 8 mth. at $1\frac{1}{2}$% per annum.
7. £151 17s. 6d. in 3 yr. 4 mth. at $3\frac{1}{3}$% per annum.
8. £687 10s. in 73 days at $3\frac{1}{2}$% per annum.
9. £733 6s. 8d. in 146 days at $3\frac{3}{4}$% per annum.
10. £250 16s. 8d. in 2 yr. 292 dy. at 5% per annum.
11. £312 10s. from 26th June, 1955, to 19th November, 1955, at 4% per annum.
12. £178 17s. from 17th April, 1955, to 23rd December, 1955, at $3\frac{1}{2}$% per annum.

Find the amount of:

13. £375 in 4 years at 2% per annum.
14. £450 in $4\frac{1}{2}$ years at 4% per annum.
15. £361 in 5 years at $2\frac{1}{2}$% per annum.
16. £624 in $5\frac{1}{3}$ years at $3\frac{3}{4}$% per annum.
17. £116 5s. in 1 yr. 73 dy. at $2\frac{1}{2}$% per annum.
18. £182 10s. in 100 dy. at $3\frac{1}{3}$% per annum.

19. £102 4s. from 11th January, 1955, to 21st April, 1955, at 2½% per annum.

20. £483 12s. 6d. from 14th June to 21st November of the same year at 3¾% per annum.

To find the Rate Per Cent. (R)

Example 3. The Interest on £375 for 4 years is £67 10s. Find the rate of interest per cent.

Interest on £375 for 4 years = £67 10s. = £67½

$$\therefore \text{ Interest on £100 for 1 year} = £\frac{\overset{9}{\cancel{135}}}{2} \times \frac{\overset{1}{\cancel{100}}}{\cancel{375}} \times \frac{1}{\cancel{4}}$$

$$= £4\tfrac{1}{2}$$

$$\therefore \text{ Rate of Interest} = 4\tfrac{1}{2}\%$$

Example 4. At what rate per cent. Simple Interest will £450 amount to £486 in 2 yr. 8 mth.?

Interest on £450 for 2⅔ years = £(486 − 450) = £36

$$\therefore \text{ Interest on £100 for 1 year} = £\overset{4}{\cancel{36}} \times \frac{\overset{1}{\cancel{100}}}{\cancel{450}} \times \frac{3}{\cancel{8}}$$

$$= £3$$

$$\therefore \text{ Rate of Interest} = 3\%$$

EXERCISE 15B

1. At what rate per cent. per annum will £560 gain £78 8s. interest in 4 years?

2. At what rate per cent. per annum will £367 10s. gain £73 10s. interest in 8 years?

3. At what rate per cent. per annum will £340 gain £6 7s. 6d. interest in 9 months?

4. A moneylender charged 1*d*. per week on a loan of £6 10*s*. What was his rate per cent. per annum? (1 year = 52 weeks.)

5. The simple interest on 5*s*. for 2 yr. 8 mth. is $3\frac{1}{2}d$. Find the rate per cent. per annum.

6. At what rate per cent. per annum will £333 10*s*. amount to £383 10*s*. 6*d*. in 4 years?

7. If £712 10*s*. amounts to £771 17*s*. 6*d*. in $2\frac{1}{2}$ years at simple interest, find the rate per cent.

8. A man borrows £160 on condition that he pays back £169 after 9 months. At what rate per cent. per annum is interest charged?

9. Find the rate per cent. per annum simple interest at which £850 will amount to £1,147 10*s*. in 7 years.

10. At what rate per cent. per annum simple interest will 16*s*. amount to 26*s*. in 12 years?

To find the Time (T)

Example 5. In what time will £250 produce £52 10*s*. at $3\frac{1}{2}\%$ per annum simple interest?

Interest on £250 in 1 year at $3\frac{1}{2}\% = £\dfrac{7}{2} \times \dfrac{\overset{5}{\cancel{250}}}{\cancel{100}} = £8\ 15s.$

i.e. £250 produces £8 15*s*. simple interest in 1 year

$\therefore$ £250 produces £52 10*s*. simple interest in $1 \times \dfrac{52\frac{1}{2}}{8\frac{3}{4}}$

$$= \dfrac{\overset{3}{\cancel{105}} \times \overset{2}{\cancel{4}}}{2 \times \underset{1}{\cancel{35}}}$$

$$= 6 \text{ years}$$

$\therefore$ Required Time = 6 years

Example 6. In what time will £850 amount to £892 10*s*. at $2\frac{1}{2}\%$ per annum simple interest?

Interest on £850 in 1 year at $2\frac{1}{2}\% = £\dfrac{5}{2} \times \dfrac{\overset{850}{\cancel{850}}}{\cancel{100}} = £21\ 5s.$

Total Interest produced $= £(892\frac{1}{2} - 850) = £42\ 10s.$

Hence, £850 produces £21 5*s*. simple interest in 1 year

$\therefore$ £850 produces £42 10s. simple interest in $1 \times \dfrac{42\frac{1}{2}}{21\frac{1}{4}}$

$= 2$ years

$\therefore$ Required Time $= 2$ years

EXERCISE 15c

1. In how many years will £450 produce £49 10s. simple interest at $2\frac{3}{4}\%$ per annum?

2. In what time will the simple interest on £750 amount to £101 5s. at $4\frac{1}{2}\%$ per annum?

3. The simple interest on £230 in a certain time amounts to £60 7s. 6d. at $3\frac{1}{2}\%$ per annum. What is this time?

4. In what time will the simple interest on £785 5s. become £52 7s. at $3\frac{1}{3}\%$ per annum?

5. In how many days will £27 7s. 6d. earn 12s. 6d. simple interest at the rate of $8\frac{1}{3}\%$ per annum?

6. In what time will £110 amount to £132 at $3\frac{3}{4}\%$ per annum simple interest?

7. Find the time in which £250 amounts to £257 10s. at 4% per annum simple interest.

8. In how many years will £5,250 amount to £6,212 10s. at $3\frac{1}{3}\%$ per annum simple interest?

9. Find the time in which £15 10s. will amount to £21 6s. 3d. at $2\frac{1}{2}\%$ per annum simple interest.

10. In how many years will a sum of money double itself at $2\frac{1}{2}\%$ per annum simple interest?

To find the Principal (P). (A)

Example 7. The simple interest on a sum of money invested for 3 years 9 months at 3% is £37 10s. Find the sum invested.

Interest on £100 for $3\frac{3}{4}$ years at 3% $= £11\frac{1}{4}$
i.e. $£11\frac{1}{4} =$ interest on £100

$\therefore £37\frac{1}{2} =$ interest on £100 $\times \dfrac{37\frac{1}{2}}{11\frac{1}{4}}$

i.e. $£100 \times \dfrac{\overset{5}{\cancel{75}} \times \overset{2}{\cancel{4}}}{\underset{1}{\cancel{2}} \times \underset{3}{\cancel{45}}} = £333\frac{1}{3}$

$\therefore$ Required Sum $= £333$ 6s. 8d.

EXERCISE 15D

1. Find the sum which will produce £126 simple interest in 3 years at 5% per annum.

2. What sum will yield £165 if invested for $5\frac{1}{2}$ years at 4% per annum simple interest?

3. The interest on a certain sum for 5 years at $4\frac{1}{2}$% per annum is £803 5s. Find the sum.

4. What sum invested for 2 years 8 months at 4% per annum will yield £80 simple interest?

5. Find the sum which will produce £7 14s. simple interest in 1 year 4 months at $4\frac{2}{5}$% per annum.

6. What sum of money will yield £162 simple interest in $2\frac{1}{2}$ years at $4\frac{1}{2}$% per annum?

7. The interest on a sum of money invested for 219 days at $2\frac{1}{2}$% per annum is £5 5s. Find the sum.

8. What sum will produce £2 5s. simple interest if invested for 100 days at $4\frac{1}{2}$% per annum?

9. A sum of money is invested from 7th June to 22nd August of a certain year at 5% per annum. If the interest obtained is £2 17s., find the sum.

10. If £4 14s. 6d. simple interest is obtained by the investment of a certain sum of money at $4\frac{1}{2}$% per annum from 29th July to 10th October of the same year, find the sum.

To find the Principal (P). (B)

Example 8. What Principal will amount to £406 in 4 years at 4% per annum?

Interest on £100 in 4 years at 4% = £16

i.e. Principal which amounts to £116 in 4 years at 4% = £100

∴ Principal which amounts to £406 in 4 years at 4% = £1ØØ × $\dfrac{\overset{25}{\overset{14}{4Ø6}}}{\underset{29}{\underset{1}{11\cancel{6}}}}$

= £350

∴ Required Principal = £350

EXERCISE 15E

1. What Principal will amount to £825 in 3 years at $3\frac{1}{3}$% per annum simple interest?

2. What sum of money amounts to £627 in $2\frac{1}{2}$ years at 4% per annum simple interest?

3. Find what Principal will amount to £272 5s. in 6 years at $3\frac{1}{2}$% per annum simple interest.

4. What Principal will amount to £359 2s. 6d. in 6 years at $1\frac{3}{4}$% per annum simple interest?

5. What Principal will amount to £236 10s. in 5 years at $1\frac{1}{2}$% per annum simple interest?

6. What sum will amount to £1,748 5s. in 8 years at $3\frac{1}{4}$% per annum simple interest?

7. What sum will amount to £334 15s. in 9 months at 4% per annum simple interest?

8. What sum will amount to £991 13s. 4d. in $2\frac{1}{2}$ years at $5\frac{1}{3}$% per annum simple interest?

9. What sum will amount to £3,993 7s. 6d. in $3\frac{1}{2}$ years at $4\frac{1}{2}$% per annum simple interest?

10. What sum will amount to £136 16s. 9d. in $7\frac{1}{2}$ years at $1\frac{1}{2}$% per annum simple interest?

THE POST OFFICE SAVINGS BANK*

Before leaving the subject of Simple Interest for the time being it may be useful to consider the working of the Post Office Savings Bank. This is frequently the first contact that a child makes with Banking.

Types of Account

(A) **Individual.** Any person over 7 years of age may open an account (i.e. join the bank) and make deposits and withdrawals (i.e. put **in** money and take it **out** when required).

(B) **Children.** An account may be opened on behalf of a child who is under seven years of age. The child may make withdrawals after reaching that age.

---

* Most of the information contained in this section is from the Post Office Guide 1956 and is reproduced by the kind permission of the Postmaster-General.

(C) **Joint.** Two or more people can have an account in their joint names. An application for withdrawing money must be signed by each person whose name appears on the account.

(D) **Trust.** One or more persons may open an account in trust for another person or persons also named in the account. If this account is for a child, the money cannot be withdrawn while the child is under 7 years of age.

(E) **Society.** Accounts may be opened on behalf of Friendly, Charitable, Church, Christmas, etc. Societies.

Deposits and Limits of Account

No amount may be accepted from a depositor (or joint depositor) which will

(*a*) bring his total deposits in any Savings Bank year (January 1st to December 31st) to an amount exceeding £500,

(*b*) bring the aggregate amount standing to his credit (in all accounts in his name) to a total of more than £3,000.

Note that deposits of 1*s.* and upwards may be made (except for a first deposit, when the minimum is 5*s.*), and this may be made by cash, bank cheque, money order, postal order or savings stamps.

Interest on Deposits

1. Interest at the rate of $2\frac{1}{2}\%$ per annum (i.e. $\frac{1}{2}d.$ *per* £1 *per month or* 6*d. per year*) is allowed on every *complete* £1 standing to the credit of a savings bank account and is added to the account at the close of each year ending December 31st, after which it becomes part of the Principal.

2. Money deposited bears interest from the beginning of the month *following* that in which it is received. Money withdrawn ceases to bear interest from the beginning of the month in which a withdrawal is made.

Example 9. A man deposited £50 in the Post Office Savings Bank on the last day of each month beginning on 30th June, 1955. What was the value of his account on 1st January, 1956?

The first £50 bears interest for 6 months; the second for 5 months; ...and the seventh £50 bears no interest since it has just been deposited.

Interest on £1 per month $=\frac{1}{2}d.$

$\therefore$ Interest on £50 per month $=2s.$ $1d.$

$\therefore$ Total Interest $=2s.$ $1d.$ $\times(6+5+4+3+2+1)$

$=2s.$ $1d.$ $\times 21$

$=£2$ $3s.$ $9d.$

But Total Deposit $=£50 \times 7$

$=£350$

$\therefore$ Value of account on 1st January, 1956 $=£352$ $3s.$ $9d.$

Example 10. If a man invests £200 just before 1st January of each of two successive years in the Post Office Savings Bank, what is the value of his account at the end of the second year?

Interest on £200 during 1st year $=£5$

$\therefore$ Amount of £200 at end of 1st year $=£205$

$\therefore$ Principal yielding interest during 2nd year $=£205+£200=£405$

Interest on £405 during 2nd year $=£\dfrac{405\times2\frac{1}{2}}{100}$

$$=£\dfrac{\overset{81}{\cancel{405}}\times\overset{1}{\cancel{5}}}{\underset{20}{\cancel{100}}\times2}$$

$$=£10\ 2s.\ 6d.$$

$\therefore$ Value of account at end of 2nd year $=£405+£10$ $2s.$ $6d.$

$=£415$ $2s.$ $6d.$

EXERCISE 15F

The following sums of money are invested in the Post Office Savings Bank for the given times. Find (i) the interest accruing and (ii) the amount of each sum at the end of the time.

1. £150 for 4 months.
2. £270 for 8 months.
3. £212 10s. for 9 months.
4. £218 15s. for 10 months.
5. £291 13s. 4d. for 1 year.
6. £175 from 16th January to 20th April.
7. £250 from 10th February to 5th June.
8. £156 5s. from 7th March to 18th September.

9. £280 10*s.* from 26th April to 21st October.

10. £145 16*s.* 8*d.* from 2nd May to 19th December.

11. A Christmas Savings Group collects the following sums and invests them in the Post Office Savings Bank:

June	£60	July	£70	August	£50
September	£75	October	£80	November	£120

If the interest obtained is given to charity, what is the amount of this sum, assuming interest is obtained for December.

12. Three members of a family open a joint account in the Post Office Savings Bank on January 12th, 1956, contributing £10, £15 and £20 respectively, and similar sums at the corresponding day each month thereafter. What amount should each receive if a warrant for withdrawal is given on August 8th, 1956?

13. A man invests £500 at the beginning of each of three successive years in the Post Office Savings Bank. What is the value of his account at the end of the third year?

14. One man invests £500 in the Post Office Savings Bank for 10 months. Another man invests the same sum in a total of 10 monthly instalments of £50 each. Find the difference in the interest obtained by the two men.

15. A man saves £20 a month from his salary and invests it in the Post Office Savings Bank. What is the value of his savings account at the end of a full year, assuming that he invests on the 15th day of each month?

16

Averages

The subject of 'averages' is one with which most young people are familiar nowadays. For example, boys are interested in the 'batting average' or the 'bowling average' of their favourite County cricketer. Then, at certain distinct times each year, both boys and girls become acquainted with 'examination averages'.

Consideration of a few examples will help towards some understanding of this word 'average'.

Example 1. In eight Test Match innings a leading cricketer scored 57, 23, 121, 96, 14, 37, 143 and 169 runs respectively. What was his average for the series?

Total number of runs scored = 660

Total number of innings played =   8

$$\therefore \text{ Average for the series} = \frac{\text{total number of runs scored}}{\text{total number of innings played}}$$

$$= \frac{660}{8}$$

$$= 82 \cdot 5 \text{ runs}$$

Example 2. The contributions of a certain class to a school Charities' Fund for a period of 6 weeks were 2s. 9½d., 3s. 4d., 3s. 1½d., 2s. 10d., 3s. 7d. and 3s. 10d. respectively. What is the average weekly contribution? If the total number of pupils in the class is 26, what is the average weekly contribution per pupil during this period?

Total sum contributed = 19s. 6d.

Total number of weeks = 6

$$\therefore \text{Average sum per week} = \frac{\text{total sum contributed}}{\text{total number of weeks}}$$

$$= \frac{19s.\ 6d.}{6}$$

$$= 3s.\ 3d.$$

$$\text{Total number of pupils} = 26$$

$$\therefore \text{Average per pupil per week} = \frac{3s.\ 3d.}{26}$$

$$= \frac{39d.}{26}$$

$$= 1\tfrac{1}{2}d.$$

Hence we might conclude that the

Average value of a number of things *of the same kind*

$$= \frac{\text{the total sum of them}}{\text{the total number of them}}$$

Note, too, that the total sum of a number of things

$$= \text{their average} \times \text{total number of them}$$

The average of a number of things of the same kind is sometimes referred to as their **Arithmetic Mean**.

EXERCISE 16A

Find the average of the following numbers.

1. 5, 9, 13, 17, 21   2. 12, 18, 13, 23, 31, 29
3. 11, 6, 15, 19, 9, 3, 7   4. $2\tfrac{1}{2}$, $4\tfrac{1}{4}$, $3\tfrac{3}{4}$, 6, $5\tfrac{1}{2}$
5. $8\tfrac{2}{3}$, $4\tfrac{1}{2}$, $5\tfrac{1}{4}$, $6\tfrac{5}{6}$, 7, $8\tfrac{1}{4}$ 6. 3·85, 4·30, 6·43, 5·27, 8·05

7. What is the average age of five members of an Old Men's Club who are 87, 85, 81, 78 and 74 years old respectively?

8. The following are the cricket scores of a certain batsman: 27, 69, 38, 15, 49, 73, 0, 131, 57, 31, 0, 98. Find his average.

9. The weights of a certain rowing eight are as follows: 9 st. 1 lb., 10 st., 10 st. 3 lb., 11 st. 2 lb., 12 st. 6 lb., 11 st. 5 lb., 11 st. 7 lb., 10 st. 4 lb. What is the average weight of the crew?

10. The readings on a classroom thermometer taken on a certain day at intervals of 1 hour are 53°, 56°, 56°, 57°, 58°, 61°, 63°, 60° on the Fahrenheit scale. What is the average temperature?

11. A bus travels 3 ml., 4 ml., 8 ml., 9 ml., 12 ml., 11 ml., 10 ml.,

and 7 ml. in successive quarter-hours. Find the average distance travelled in $\frac{1}{4}$ hour and hence find the average speed of the bus in miles per hour.

12. During a certain week the value of the franc in London varied from day to day as follows: 0·251d., 0·254d., 0·255d., 0·253d., 0·249d., 0·248d. If a merchant in France sold goods in this country to the value of £2 12s. 8d., how many francs should he receive if paid at the average value of the franc for the week? (To nearest franc.)

13. The takings at a cinema for six days were:

Monday	£30 8s. 10d.	Tuesday	£24 15s. 0d.
Wednesday	£37 5s. 0d.	Thursday	£26 5s. 4d.
Friday	£41 7s. 6d.	Saturday	£51 19s. 4d.

Find the average daily takings.

14. A grocer's takings for five consecutive days were £51 13s. 6d., £47 10s., £41 14s. 3d., £38 10s., and £40 12s. 3d. Find by what percentage the lowest daily takings fall short of the average.

15. A man's wage on six successive weeks is £13 19s. 2d., £14 12s., £14 1s., £14 4s. 8d., £14 8s. 4d. and £13 14s. 10d. Find his average weekly wage and hence find the percentage by which his lowest wage falls below his average wage.

There are wide variations in the method of averages which can best be appreciated by considering some further typical worked examples.

Example 3. The average monthly rainfall in a certain year was 1·59 in. The average for the last three months of the year was 1·50 in. What was the average for the first nine months?

Average rainfall for 12 months = 1·59 in.
∴ Total rainfall for 12 months = 1·59 × 12 = 19·08 in.
Average rainfall for last 3 months = 1·50 in.
∴ Total rainfall for last 3 months = 1·50 × 3 = 4·50 in.
∴ Total rainfall for first 9 months = 19·08 − 4·50 = 14·58 in.

∴ Average rainfall for first 9 months = $\dfrac{14·58}{9}$ = 1·62 in.

Example 4. The average weight of 12 men is 11 st. 9 lb. If the average weight of three of the men is 12 st. 2 lb., and the average weight of four of the others is 11 st. 11$\frac{1}{4}$ lb., what is the average weight of the remainder?

Average weight of 12 men = 11 st.   9 lb.

∴ Total weight of 12 men = 139 st. 10 lb.

Average weight of 3 men = 12 st.   2 lb.

∴ Total weight of 3 men = 36 st.   6 lb.

Average weight of 4 other men = 11 st. $11\frac{1}{4}$ lb.

∴ Total weight of 4 other men = 47 st.   3 lb.

∴ Total weight of remaining 5 men

= 139 st. 10 lb. − (36 st. 6 lb. + 47 st. 3 lb.)

= 139 st. 10 lb. − 83 st. 9 lb.

= 56 st.   1 lb.

∴ Average weight of remaining 5 men

$$= \frac{56 \text{ st. } 1 \text{ lb.}}{5}$$

= 11 st. 3 lb.

Example 5. A man bought 12 articles for £21 6s. The average price of 8 of the articles was £1 14s. $8\frac{1}{2}d$. and the average price of 3 of the remaining 4 articles was £1 15s. $2\frac{3}{4}d$. What was the price of the 12th article?

Total cost of 12 articles = £21 6s.

Average cost of 8 articles = £1 14s. $8\frac{1}{2}d$.

∴ Total cost of 8 articles = £13 17s. 8d.

Average cost of 3 other articles = £1 15s. $2\frac{3}{4}d$.

∴ Total cost of 3 other articles = £5 5s. $8\frac{1}{4}d$.

∴ Cost of 12th article = £21 6s. − (£13 17s. 8d. + £5 5s. $8\frac{1}{4}d$.)

= £21 6s. − £19 3s. $4\frac{1}{4}d$.

= £2 2s. $7\frac{3}{4}d$.

EXERCISE 16b

1. A man's average monthly expenses for a certain year were £22 14s. If his average monthly expenses for the first 9 months were £23 8s., find the average for the last 3 months.

2. The average weight of 4 men was 12 st. 3 lb. If three of them weighed 12 st. 8 lb., 11 st. 12 lb. and 11 st. 9 lb. respectively, what was the weight of the fourth man?

3. A man walks for 3 hours at the rate of 5 ml. per hour and then for $1\frac{1}{2}$ hrs. at 4 ml. per hour. Find how far he walks altogether and his average in miles per hour.

4. The average monthly profits of a firm from January to April were £416 8s. 6d. and the profits for May and June were £437 2s. and £489 4s. respectively. Find the average monthly profits for the full half-year.

5. A firm's monthly sales from July to November were £9,875, £8,963, £9,004, £9,670 and £9,866. What must be the December sales so that the monthly average for the half-year may be £9,563?

6. The average temperature for Monday, Tuesday and Wednesday was 53° F. The average for Tuesday, Wednesday and Thursday was 56° F., the temperature for Thursday being 60° F. Find the temperature on Monday.

7. The rainfall of a certain district for the first five months of a given year was 4·00 in., 12·09 in., 6·54 in., 20·79 in., 27·40 in. What rainfall for the next month would make the average for the six months 12·43 in.?

8. In a class of 18 boys and 14 girls at a certain examination, the boys' average mark was 54·2 and the girls' average mark was 67·8. Find the class average.

9. At a sale of 12 horses, the average price paid was £86 12s. 6d. The first 7 horses were sold at an average price of £92 5s. Find the average price of the remainder.

10. A firm employing 9 boys, 11 tradesmen and 2 foremen pays each boy £4 15s., each tradesman £11 8s. and each foreman £14 3s. 10d. per week. Calculate the average weekly earnings.

11. In the first part of the season a cricketer's scores were 7, 29, 0, 58, 14, 72. What was his average score? In the next 8 matches he scored an average of 26·5. What was his average score for the 14 matches?

12. A certain herring fishing fleet consists of 210 vessels, 140 of which are steam driven and the remainder are diesel driven. On a certain day the average catch for the whole fleet is 20 crans while the average for the steam vessels is 25 crans. What is the average catch of the diesel driven vessels?

13. A motorist on a journey of 72 miles does the first 40 miles at an average rate of 25 mls. per hour. At what rate must he travel the remaining distance to have an average speed of 30 mls. per hour for the whole journey?

14. In a certain month the daily average of sunshine for the first 8 days was 3·4 hours; that for the next 10 days was 4·34 hours, and for the next 6 days, 7·16 hours. Find the daily average for the remaining 7 days if the average for the month was 5·35 hours.

15. In a company of 13 boys and 8 girls, it is found that 1 boy

is 5 ft. 11 in. in height, 3 are 5 ft. $8\frac{1}{2}$ in., 4 are 5 ft. 7 in., 4 are 5 ft. $6\frac{1}{2}$ in. and 1 is 5 ft. $3\frac{3}{4}$ in. Of the girls, 1 is 5 ft. 8 in. in height, 2 are 5 ft. $6\frac{1}{2}$ in., 4 are 5 ft. $5\frac{1}{2}$ in. and 1 is 5 ft. 1 in. Find the average height of (i) the boys; (ii) the girls; (iii) the whole company (to the nearest $\frac{1}{10}$ in.).

16. The following tickets were sold for a pageant: 1,189 at £1 1s., 1,622 at 10s. 6d., 422 at 8s., 211 at 6s. 6d., 1,145 at 5s., and 1,141 at 2s. 6d. Find the total amount paid and the average price per ticket. (To nearest penny.)

17. From four successive radio appeals in 'The Week's Good Cause' these sums were obtained: £251 8s. 4d., £537 10s. 6d., £293 7s. 8d., and £331 6s. 10d. Find the average amount contributed for these four appeals. What must be the average for the next two appeals to make the average for each of the six appeals £360 10s.?

18. A batsman's average for 8 cricket innings was 59·5 runs. He played 2 more innings and his average now became 57·2. If in the first extra innings he scored 23 runs, what did he score in the second extra innings?

19. A cricketer has an average of 65 runs for 35 completed innings.

(i) In his first two matches he scored 8 and 14 runs, and in his last three matches he scored 0, 205 and 20 runs. Find his average during the intermediate period.

(ii) In the matches following he scored 265 more runs and his average fell by 1·5 runs. How many completed innings did he take to score the 265 runs?

20. A merchant mixes 16 lb. of coffee at 6s. 9d. per lb., 6 lb. at 10s. per lb. and 20 lb. at 10s. 6d. per lb. Find the average price per lb. of the mixture. If he wishes to gain £2 2s. on selling the coffee, what price must he charge per lb.?

21. A traveller's expenses for the first 5 months of a year are £8 4s. 4d., £7 9s. 10d., £6 13s. 4d., £7 3s. 10d., and £7 18s. 8d. His average monthly expenses for the next 7 months are £7 4s. Find the average for the first 5 months and his average monthly expenditure over the whole year.

22. A train runs 16 miles in 24 minutes. What is its average speed in miles per hour? On a particular journey, after running at its usual speed for 4 miles, it has to run the next $\frac{1}{2}$ mile at 10 miles per hour. What must be its average speed on the rest of the journey if it is completed in the usual time?

23. During the months of September, October and November a

motorist covered 2,535 miles and used 89 gallons of petrol. Find, correct to one decimal place, his average mileage per gallon.

Over this period he paid 7s. 6d. per week for garaging and allowed £15 for depreciation of his car, and his other expenses, including the cost of petrol, amounted to £56 10s. 5d. Find, to the nearest farthing, the average cost of his motoring per mile.

24. A householder uses 5 bags of coal per week during the six months October to March (26 weeks) and 2 bags per week during the months April to September (26 weeks). The winter price is 6s. 10d. per bag and the summer price is 6s. 2d. per bag. Find the yearly coal bill and the average price per bag correct to the nearest halfpenny.

25. A local bus company decides to discontinue a service on a certain route unless the average number of passengers during a particular week is 475 a day. The daily average over the period Monday to Saturday is 511. What is the least number that must travel on Sunday in order to have the service maintained?

Assuming the average fare on this route is 5d. per passenger, find the average number of persons that travelled daily during a week when the gross takings amounted to £133 14s. 7d.

17

Decimalization of Money at Sight and Practice

(A) Decimalization of Money AT SIGHT

In Chapter 6 we have already given details of the decimalization of money.

Example 1. Express £4 13s. 7½d. as a decimal of £1.

$$
\begin{array}{r|l}
12 & 7 \cdot 5 \quad \text{pence} \\
\hline
20 & 13 \cdot 625 \quad \text{shillings} \\
\hline
& £4 \cdot 68125
\end{array}
$$

∴ £4 13s. 7½d. = £4·68125

= £4·681 (correct to 3rd decimal place)

We are now interested in finding a method which will enable us to express such a sum of money as a decimal of £1 (correct to 3rd decimal place) **without** actual working.

Since $2s. = \frac{1}{10}$ of £1 = £0·1

and $1s. = \frac{1}{2}$ of $2s.$ = £0·05

the following table can be completed.

Shillings	Dec. of £1	Shillings	Dec. of £1	Shillings	Dec. of £1
1	0·05	8	0·40	15	0·75
2	0·10	9	0·45	16	0·80
3	0·15	10	0·50	17	0·85
4	0·20	11	0·55	18	0·90
5	0·25	12	0·60	19	0·95
6	0·30	13	0·65		
7	0·35	14	0·70		

Thus, to express shillings as a decimal of £1 the following rule will be useful:

Multiply the number of shillings by 5 and call the result hundredths of £1.

Continuing this process, $6d. = \frac{1}{2}$ of $1s. = \frac{1}{2}$ of £0·05 = £0·025

Example 2. Express 14s. 6d. as a decimal of £1.

$$\left.\begin{array}{l} 14s. = £0·7 \\ 6d. = £0·025 \end{array}\right\} \therefore 14s.\ 6d. = £0·725$$

Example 3. Express £1 15s. 6d. as a decimal of £1.

$$\left.\begin{array}{l} 15s. = £0·75 \\ 6d. = £0·025 \end{array}\right\} \therefore £1\ 15s.\ 6d. = £1·775$$

So far we have been dealing only with shillings and sixpences, thus leaving untouched by our method a wide range of frequently occurring sums of money. To deal with these we require quite a different method.

Thus, 1 farthing $= £\frac{1}{960} = 0·0010416\ldots$
i.e. 1 farthing $= 0·001$ (correct to 3rd decimal place)
Similarly, 1 halfpenny $= 0·002$ (correct to 3rd decimal place)
and 3 farthings $= 0·003$ (correct to 3rd decimal place)

Example 4. Express 17s. $6\frac{3}{4}d.$ as a decimal of £1 (correct to 3rd decimal place).

$$\left.\begin{array}{l} 17s. = £0·85 \\ 6d. = £0·025 \\ \tfrac{3}{4}d. = £0·003 \end{array}\right\} \therefore 17s.\ 6\tfrac{3}{4}d. = £0·878$$

But, again, in the above example, we are dealing with 6d. which gives a convenient decimal of £1.

Suppose we consider 3d. expressed as a decimal of £1 by two methods:

(i) $3d. = \frac{1}{2}$ of $6d. = \frac{1}{2}$ of £0·025 = £0·0125
$= £0·013$ (to 3rd decimal place)
(ii) $3d. = 12$ farthings $= £0·012$ (to 3rd decimal place)

It is clear that this requires further investigation.

In the following comparative tables

(a) first column gives sum to be decimalized;
(b) second column gives decimalized sum using normal method;
(c) third column gives decimalized sum using farthing method.

(A)

(a) Sum	(b) Decimal of £1	(c) Decimal of £1
$1\frac{1}{2}d.$	£0·006	£0·006
$3d.$	£0·013	£0·012
$4\frac{1}{2}d.$	£0·019	£0·018
$6d.$	£0·025	£0·024
$7\frac{1}{2}d.$	£0·031	£0·030
$9d.$	£0·038	£0·036
$10\frac{1}{2}d.$	£0·044	£0·042

Note that the decimalization is correct to the 3rd decimal place in column (b).

Consider more minutely a similar table for numbers between $\frac{1}{4}d.$ and $3d.$

(B)

(a) Sum	(b) Decimal of £1	(c) Decimal of £1
$\frac{1}{4}d.$	£0·001	£0·001
$\frac{1}{2}d.$	£0·002	£0·002
$\frac{3}{4}d.$	£0·003	£0·003
$1d.$	£0·004	£0·004
$1\frac{1}{4}d.$	£0·005	£0·005
$1\frac{1}{2}d.$	£0·006	£0·006
$1\frac{3}{4}d.$	£0·007	£0·007
$2d.$	£0·008	£0·008
$2\frac{1}{4}d.$	£0·009	£0·009
$2\frac{1}{2}d.$	£0·010	£0·010
$2\frac{3}{4}d.$	£0·011	£0·011
$3d.$	£0·013	£0·012

It will be seen from table (B) that for sums **from $\frac{1}{4}d.$ to $2\frac{3}{4}d.$** (inclusive) the decimal of £1 obtained using the 'farthing' method agrees with that obtained by more accurate methods (to three decimal places).

Using table (A) we see that **from 3d. to $8\frac{3}{4}d.$** (inclusive) there is a difference of £0·001 between the two. **This necessitates a correction of £0·001 being added to the decimalized sum** obtained using the 'farthings' method.

Similarly, **from 9d. to $11\frac{3}{4}d.$ (inclusive) a correction of £0·002 should be added.**

Example 5. Express 13s. $5\frac{1}{4}d$. (i) as a decimal of £1 correct to 3rd decimal place, (ii) as a percentage of £1 to nearest whole number.

$$13s. = £0 \cdot 65$$
$$5\frac{1}{4}d. = 21 \text{ farthings} = £0 \cdot 022 \text{ (adding £0·001 as correction)}$$
$$\text{(i)} \therefore 13s. \ 5\frac{1}{4}d. = £0 \cdot 672$$
$$\text{(ii)} \therefore 13s. \ 5\frac{1}{4}d. = 67\% \text{ of £1}$$

Example 6. Express £2 19s. $10\frac{3}{4}d$. (i) as a decimal of £1 correct to 3rd decimal place, (ii) as a percentage of £1 to nearest $\frac{1}{10}$th.

$$19s. = £0 \cdot 95$$
$$10\frac{3}{4}d. = 43 \text{ farthings} = £0 \cdot 045 \text{ (adding £0·002 as correction)}$$
$$\text{(i)} \therefore £2 \ 19s. \ 10\frac{3}{4}d. = £2 \cdot 995$$
$$\text{(ii)} \therefore £2 \ 19s. \ 10\frac{3}{4}d. = 299 \cdot 5\% \text{ of £1}$$

EXERCISE 17A. *Oral*

Express each of the following sums as an **exact** decimal of £1.

1. 4s. 6d.	**2.** 8s. 6d.	**3.** 16s. 6d.
4. 3s. 6d.	**5.** 9s. 6d.	**6.** 17s. 6d.
7. 19s. 6d.	**8.** £1 10s. 3d.	**9.** £2 12s. 9d.
10. £3 13s. 3d.	**11.** £1 17s. 9d.	**12.** £2 9s. 3d.

Express each of the following sums as a decimal of £1 correct to 3rd decimal place.

13. 8s. $6\frac{1}{4}d$.	**14.** 10s. $6\frac{1}{2}d$.	**15.** 12s. $6\frac{3}{4}d$.
16. 18s. $6\frac{1}{2}d$.	**17.** 7s. $6\frac{3}{4}d$.	**18.** 11s. $6\frac{1}{4}d$.
19. 15s. $6\frac{1}{2}d$.	**20.** 19s. $6\frac{1}{4}d$.	**21.** £1 12s. $6\frac{1}{2}d$.
22. £3 13s. $6\frac{3}{4}d$.	**23.** £5 17s. $6\frac{1}{4}d$.	**24.** £7 19s. $6\frac{1}{2}d$.
25. £2 7s. $3\frac{1}{4}d$.		

EXERCISE 17B

Express each of the following sums, (i) as a decimal of £1 correct to 3rd decimal place, (ii) as a percentage of £1 to nearest $\frac{1}{10}$th, and check **odd** numbers by the method of worked example 1.

1. 5s. $2\frac{1}{4}d$.	**2.** 7s. $3\frac{3}{4}d$.	**3.** 12s. $7\frac{1}{2}d$.
4. 13s. $10\frac{1}{4}d$.	**5.** 15s. $5\frac{3}{4}d$.	**6.** 16s. $9\frac{1}{2}d$.
7. 18s. $11\frac{1}{4}d$.	**8.** 19s. $4\frac{3}{4}d$.	**9.** £1 5s. $8\frac{1}{4}d$.
10. £4 7s. $9\frac{1}{2}d$.	**11.** £5 9s. $10\frac{1}{4}d$.	**12.** £8 11s. $11\frac{1}{2}d$.
13. £3 13s. $1\frac{1}{2}d$.	**14.** £2 15s. $4\frac{1}{4}d$.	**15.** £6 17s. $2\frac{1}{2}d$.

(B) De-decimalization of Money AT SIGHT

Example 7. Express £2·765 in £ *s. d.* to the nearest halfpenny.

$$\begin{array}{r} \text{£2·765} \\ 20 \\ \hline 15·300 \text{ shillings} \\ 12 \\ \hline 3·6 \text{ pence} \end{array}$$

$\therefore$ £2·765 = £2 15s. $3\frac{1}{2}d$.

So far this is the only method of de-decimalization that we have known. The problem now is to discover a method which will enable us to perform this operation **at sight**.

It seems fairly obvious that such a method will consist of reversing the operation which has just been discussed for decimalization at sight.

Thus, £0·001 = $\frac{1}{4}d$.; £0·002 = $\frac{1}{2}d$.; £0·003 = $\frac{3}{4}d$., etc., and this can be extended with certain corrections.

We have seen that, in decimalization, for sums of money from

$\frac{1}{4}d$. to $2\frac{3}{4}d$., **no** correction is required;

3d. to $8\frac{3}{4}d$., *a correction of* £0·001 *must be* **added**;

9d. to $11\frac{3}{4}d$., *a correction of* £0·002 *must be* **added**.

Hence, in de-decimalization, for sums of money from

£0·001 to £0·012, **no** correction is required to convert to farthings;

£0·013 to £0·037, *a correction of 1 farthing must be* **subtracted** from the sum;

£0·038 to £0·049, *a correction of 2 farthings must be* **subtracted** from the sum.

Example 8. Express £0·028 in pence correct to the nearest farthing.

Number of farthings = 28
Correction in farthings = 1

$\therefore$ Sum in farthings = 27 = $6\frac{3}{4}d$.

Example 9. Express £0·483 in £ *s. d.* correct to the nearest farthing.

£0·483 = £0·45 + £0·033
= 9s. + 32 farthings
= 9s. 8d.

Example 10. Express £5·697 in £ *s. d.* correct to the nearest farthing.

$$£5·697 = £5·65 + £0·047$$
$$= £5\ 13s. + 45\ \text{farthings}$$
$$= £5\ 13s.\ 11\tfrac{1}{4}d.$$

EXERCISE 17c

Using the method of worked example 7, express each of the following sums in £ *s. d.* correct to the nearest farthing.

1. £0·217	**2.** £0·728	**3.** £0·861	**4.** £0·983
5. £1·814	**6.** £2·972	**7.** £4·531	**8.** £5·662
9. £7·743	**10.** £8·218		

EXERCISE 17d

Orally or otherwise, express each of the following sums in £ *s. d.* correct to the nearest farthing.

1. £0·328	**2.** £0·839	**3.** £0·972	**4.** £0·594
5. £1·925	**6.** £3·083	**7.** £5·642	**8.** £6·774
9. £8·854	**10.** £9·329	**11.** £10·176	**12.** £11·381
13. £12·492	**14.** £14·586	**15.** £16·697	

The foregoing processes provide a useful method for finding percentages of given sums of money.

Example 11. Find the value of 1% of £368 16*s.* correct to the nearest farthing.

$$£368\ 16s. = £368·8$$
$$\therefore\ 1\%\ \text{of}\ £368\ 16s. = \tfrac{1}{100}\ \text{of}\ £368·8$$
$$= £3·688$$
$$= £3\ 13s.\ 9d.$$

Example 12. Find the value of 4% of £213 13*s.* 5*d.* correct to the nearest farthing.

$$£213\ 13s.\ 5d. = £213·671$$
$$\therefore\ 4\%\ \text{of}\ £213\ 13s.\ 5d. = £2·13671 \times 4$$
$$= £8·54684$$
$$= £8·547$$
$$= £8\ 10s.\ 11\tfrac{1}{4}d.$$

EXERCISE 17E

Evaluate the following correct to the nearest farthing.

1. 2% of £125 12s.　　　　　　2. 3% of £236 18s.
3. 6% of £457 13s.　　　　　　4. 7% of £568 17s.
5. 8% of £679 19s.　　　　　　6. 9% of £314 10s. 6d.
7. $2\frac{1}{2}$% of £425 13s. 6d.　　　8. $4\frac{1}{2}$% of £812 16s. 4d.
9. $7\frac{1}{2}$% of £923 17s. 7d.　　　10. $12\frac{1}{2}$% of £968 15s. 2d.

(C) Practice—Simple

Example 13. Find the cost of 276 articles at £2 16s. $4\frac{1}{2}$d. each.

£	s.	d.
2	16	$4\frac{1}{2}$
		276

£777	19	6

225	103	138
552	1656	1104
777	276	12)1242
	20)4519	103..6
	225..19	

Hitherto this is the method that has been adopted for such questions.

Now we will discuss the method of **Practice** which is based on the **aliquot** parts of £1.

An aliquot part of £1 is any sum which will divide into £1 without remainder. It is, therefore,

(i) a vulgar fraction of £1;
(ii) a vulgar fraction with numerator unity.

For example, 5s., 6s. 8d., 10s., etc., are aliquot parts of £1, but 8s., 7s. 6d., 15s. 3d., etc., are not.

However, any sum of money can be divided up into aliquot parts of £1.

Thus, the sum in worked example 13 can be written,

£2 16s. $4\frac{1}{2}$d. = £2 + 10s. + 5s. + 1s. + 3d. + $1\frac{1}{2}$d.

Note that each of these aliquot parts can be obtained from the preceding one by a simple division, and this is one of the essential features of the method of Simple Practice.

Example 14.

Find, by Practice, the cost of 276 articles at £2 16s. $4\frac{1}{2}d.$ each.

			£	s.	d.	
(A)	Cost at £1	=	276	0	0	
	,, ,, £2	=	552	0	0	
	,, ,, 10s.	=	138	0	0	$10s. = \frac{1}{4}$ of £2
	,, ,, 5s.	=	69	0	0	$5s. = \frac{1}{2}$ of 10s.
	,, ,, 1s.	=	13	16	0	$1s. = \frac{1}{5}$ of 5s.
	,, ,, 3d.	=	3	9	0	$3d. = \frac{1}{4}$ of 1s.
	,, ,, $1\frac{1}{2}d.$	=	1	14	6	$1\frac{1}{2}d. = \frac{1}{2}$ of 3d
∴	Cost at £2 16s. $4\frac{1}{2}d.$	=	£777	19	6	

Note (i) that it is advisable to draw line (A) right across the page since the sum of money appearing above it does not form part of the real question;

(ii) that this division of the working into three parts makes not only for neatness but also for accuracy.

Example 15.

Find, by Practice, the cost of 533 articles at £3 17s. $9\frac{1}{2}d.$ each.

			£	s.	d.	
	Cost at £1	=	533	0	0	
	,, ,, £3	=	1,599	0	0	
	,, ,, 10s.	=	266	10	0	$10s. = \frac{1}{6}$ of £3
	,, ,, 5s.	=	133	5	0	$5s. = \frac{1}{2}$ of 10s.
	,, ,, 2s. 6d.	=	66	12	6	$2s. 6d. = \frac{1}{2}$ of 5s.
	,, ,, 3d.	=	6	13	3	$3d. = \frac{1}{10}$ of 2s. 6d.
	,, ,, $\frac{1}{2}d.$	=	1	2	$2\frac{1}{2}$	$\frac{1}{2}d. = \frac{1}{6}$ of 3d.
∴	Cost at £3 17s. $9\frac{1}{2}d.$	=	£2,073	2	$11\frac{1}{2}$	

Example 18a. **Express £3 15s. 10d. as a decimal of £1 correct to 4 decimal places.**

Hence find the cost of 1 ton 15 cwt. 2 qr. 21 lb. at £3 15s. 10d. per ton correct to the nearest penny.

$$
\begin{array}{r|l}
12 & 10 \\
20 & 15 \cdot 8333 \\
\hline
& 3 \cdot 7917
\end{array}
$$

∴ £3 15s. 10d. = £3·7917

Cost of		1 ton	=	£3·7917	
,,	,,	10 cwt.	=	1·8959	10 cwt. = $\frac{1}{2}$ of 1 ton
,,	,,	5 cwt.	=	0·9480	5 cwt. = $\frac{1}{2}$ of 10 cwt.
,,	,,	2 qr.	=	0·0948	2 qr. = $\frac{1}{10}$ of 5 cwt.
,,	,,	14 lb.	=	0·0237	14 lb. = $\frac{1}{4}$ of 2 qr.
,,	,,	7 lb.	=	0·0119	7 lb. = $\frac{1}{2}$ of 14 lb.
∴ Total Cost			=	£6·7660	

But £6·766 = £6 15s. 4d.

∴ Cost of 1 ton 15 cwt. 2 qr. 21 lb. at £3 15s. 10d. per ton
= £6 15s. 4d.

Note, that in the above example the sum of money is decimalized to 4 decimal places and the whole question is worked to that degree of accuracy so that the final answer may be found correct to the 3rd decimal place, thus ensuring an accurate answer, since we are not dealing with a quantity greater than 10 tons.

This example may be done in the reverse way.

Example 18b. **Express 1 ton 15 cwt. 2 qr. 21 lb. as a decimal of 1 ton correct to 4 decimal places.**

Hence find the cost of 1 ton 15 cwt. 2 qr. 21 lb. at £3 15s. 10d. per ton.

$$
\begin{array}{r|l}
4 & 2 \cdot 75 \quad \text{qr.} \\
20 & 15 \cdot 6875 \quad \text{cwt.} \\
\hline
& 1 \cdot 7844 \quad \text{ton}
\end{array}
$$

∴ 1 ton 15 cwt. 2 qr. 21 lb. = 1·7844 tons

Cost at £1	=	£1·7844	
Cost at £3	=	£5·3532	
,, ,, 10s.	=	0·8922	$10s. = \frac{1}{6}$ of £3
,, ,, 5s.	=	0·4461	$5s. = \frac{1}{2}$ of $10s.$
,, ,, 10d.	=	0·0744	$10d. = \frac{1}{6}$ of $5s.$
∴ Cost at £1 15s. 10d.	=	£6·7659	
	=	£6 15s. 4d.	

∴ Cost of 1 ton 15 cwt. 2 qr. 21 lb. at £3 15s. 10d. per ton
= £6 15s. 4d.

EXERCISE 17H

Find, by Practice, correct to the nearest penny, the cost of:

1. 1 cwt. 2 qr. 14 lb. at 5s. 3d. per cwt.
2. 2 cwt. 3 qr. 11 lb. at 6s. 9d. per cwt.
3. 3 cwt. 1 qr. 21 lb. at 14s. 8d. per cwt.
4. 2 cwt. 3 qr. 21 lb. at £1 11s. 8d. per cwt.
5. 3 cwt. 2 st. 12 lb. at £2 16s. 6d. per cwt.
6. 1 ton 5 cwt. 3 qr. 21 lb. at £3 15s. per ton
7. 2 tons 10 cwt. 1 qr. 14 lb. at £2 12s. 6d. per ton
8. 3 tons 15 cwt. 4 st. 7 lb. at £4 13s. 4d. per ton
9. 2 tons 6 cwt. 1 qr. 21 lb. at £1 6s. 8d. per ton
10. 1 ton 8 cwt. 3 qr. 7 lb. at £5 16s. 8d. per ton
11. 4 tons 12 cwt. 4 st. 10 lb. at £7 3s. 4d. per ton
12. 3 tons 14 cwt. 1 qr. 12 lb. at £4 14s. 10d. per ton
13. 1 ton 16 cwt. 5 st. 2 lb. at £6 15s. 5d. per ton
14. 2 tons 18 cwt. 3 qr. 18 lb. at £8 16s. 4d. per ton
15. 5 tons 19 cwt. 1 qr. 20 lb. at £10 19s. 7d. per ton

Costing

(A) Business Accounts

Much of the time each day is normally taken up with buying and selling the necessities of life. Week by week bills have to be paid for goods bought from the butcher, baker, grocer or fruiterer, etc.

From the point of view of the shopkeeper (**seller**) it is essential that a careful check is kept on all goods bought and sold. Thus **accounts** are necessary. These are simply the writings which form a record of every transaction carried through by the shopkeeper. An account is rendered when the shopkeeper sends to the customer (**buyer**) a detailed statement of all the articles bought by the latter with their appropriate cost.

The 'frills' of a detailed account usually form the heading bearing the shopkeeper's name, address, telephone number, etc. Thereafter there is ample space for writing out the truly arithmetical part of the account usually referred to as the Bill.

Example 1.

John Jones & Son, Grocer

34, Brown Street,

ANYTOWN   *Tel.* Anytown 231

Date   *Customer's Name: Mrs. James Smith*

1/10/56		£	s.	d.
	2½ stone sugar at 7½d. per lb.	1	1	10½
	¾ lb. butter at 4s. 2d. per lb.		3	1½
	6 lb. flour at 8s. 2d. per stone		3	6
	1½ doz. eggs at 6s. 3d. per dozen		9	4½
	¾ stone oatmeal at £3 5s. 4d. per cwt.		6	1½
		£2	4	0

From the foregoing it appears that all the arithmetical working is done mentally. This may or may not be true—more often the shopkeeper or his assistant makes use of any available scrap of paper to do the actual working.

Hence, in the example now given, opportunity is taken to set out the working in a reasonable way.

Example 2. Find the total cost of the following items:

	£	s.	d.
1. $5\frac{1}{4}$ lb. butter at £23 6s. 8d. per cwt.	1	1	$10\frac{1}{2}$
2. $2\frac{3}{4}$ doz. eggs at 5s. 6d. per dozen		15	$1\frac{1}{2}$
3. $4\frac{1}{2}$ lb. cheese at £3 3s. 8d. per cheese of 36 lb.		7	$11\frac{1}{2}$
4. $6\frac{1}{4}$ gall. milk at $7\frac{1}{2}d.$ per pint	1	11	3
	£3	16	$2\frac{1}{2}$

Working:

(1) $£23\frac{1}{3} \times \dfrac{5\frac{1}{4}}{112}$

$$= £\dfrac{\overset{35}{\cancel{70}}}{3} \times \dfrac{\overset{7}{21}}{\underset{16}{\underset{2}{4}} \times 112} \overset{1}{}$$

$$= £1\frac{3}{32}$$

(2) $\dfrac{11}{4} \times \dfrac{11}{2}s.$

$$= \dfrac{121}{8}s.$$

$$= 15\frac{1}{8}s.$$

(3) $63\frac{2}{3}s. \times \dfrac{4\frac{1}{2}}{36}$

$$= \dfrac{191}{3}s. \times \dfrac{\overset{1}{\cancel{9}}}{2 \times \underset{4}{36}}$$

$$= \dfrac{191}{24}s. = 7\frac{23}{24}s.$$

(4) $\dfrac{5}{8}s. \times \dfrac{25 \times \overset{1}{\cancel{8}}}{4}$

$$= \dfrac{125}{4}$$

$$= 31\frac{1}{4}s.$$

It is advisable, in the interests of accuracy, to set down the essentials of the working in this clearly numbered and tabulated form.

Example 3. If a customer is allowed a discount of $2\frac{1}{2}\%$ on material bought, what is the cost to her of the following items:

	£	s.	d.
1. $5\frac{1}{2}$ yd. calico at 3s. 3d. per yd.	.	17	$10\frac{1}{2}$
2. $2\frac{1}{4}$ yd. velvet at 15s. 6d. per yd.	1	14	$10\frac{1}{2}$
3. $4\frac{3}{4}$ yd. flannel at 5s. 6d. per yd.	1	6	$1\frac{1}{2}$
4. $7\frac{1}{2}$ yd. ribbon at 3s. 5d. per yd.	1	5	$7\frac{1}{2}$
	£5	4	6
*Discount of $2\frac{1}{2}\%$ $(=\frac{1}{40})$		2	7
	£5	1	11

Working:			
(1) $16/3$	(2) $31/0$	(3) $22/0$	(4) $23/11$
$1/7\frac{1}{2}$	$3/10\frac{1}{2}$	$4/1\frac{1}{2}$	$1/8\frac{1}{2}$
$\overline{17/10\frac{1}{2}}$	$\overline{34/10\frac{1}{2}}$	$\overline{26/1\frac{1}{2}}$	$\overline{25/7\frac{1}{2}}$

* *Note* (i) that the discount given is correct to the appropriate penny;

(ii) that, since $6d.=£\frac{1}{40}$, the discount can be obtained simply by calling the £'s and fractions of £1, sixpences and fractions of a sixpence.

Thus, discount $= 5\cdot225$ sixpences

EXERCISE 18A

Find the total cost of the following items:

1. 192 pencils at $2s.\ 4\frac{1}{2}d.$ per dozen
   38 books at $3s.\ 3d.$ each
   74 rubbers at 2 for $3d.$
   $7\frac{1}{4}$ doz. penholders at $2\frac{1}{2}d.$ each

2. 10 yd. lino at $7s.\ 10\frac{1}{2}d.$ per yd.
   30 stair rods at $37s.\ 6d.$ per dozen
   36 lb. paint at $3s.\ 7\frac{1}{2}d.$ per lb.
   120 yd. tape at $4\frac{1}{2}d.$ per ft.

3. $3\frac{1}{2}$ doz. knives at $3s.\ 1\frac{1}{2}d.$ each
   32 pails at $7s.\ 8d.$ each
   15 doz. candles at $3s.\ 4\frac{1}{2}d.$ per doz.
   56 plates at $1s.\ 7d.$ each

4. 3 lb. 12 oz. wool at $1s.\ 4\frac{1}{2}d.$ per oz.
   $17\frac{1}{2}$ yd. cloth at $13s.\ 7d.$ per yd.
   648 buttons at $22s.\ 9d.$ per gross
   153 reels cotton at $5s.\ 4d.$ per dozen reels

5. $5\frac{1}{2}$ lb. butter at $4s.\ 1d.$ per lb.
   $3\frac{1}{2}$ doz. eggs at $4s.\ 9d.$ per doz.
   $7\frac{1}{2}$ lb. bacon at $3s.\ 10d.$ per lb.
   $14\frac{1}{2}$ lb. jam at $1s.\ 7d.$ per lb.

6. 25 lb. oatmeal at $8\frac{1}{2}d.$ per lb.
   7 st. sugar at $7\frac{1}{2}d.$ per lb.
   26 lb. tea at $7s.\ 4d.$ per lb.
   4 st. $10\frac{1}{2}$ lb. potatoes at $1s.\ 7d.$ per st.

7. $3\frac{1}{2}$ lb. tea at 7s. 3d. per lb.
$4\frac{1}{2}$ oz. tobacco at £3 10s. per lb.
$5\frac{1}{2}$ pints fuel at 3s. 8d. per gallon
5 score eggs at 5s. 3d. per dozen

8. $15\frac{1}{2}$ doz. tins cooking fat at 2s. 1d. per tin
$38\frac{1}{2}$ lb. salt at 1s. 2d. per quarter stone
5 boxes of raisins, each weighing 1 cwt. 1 qr., at £7 10s. per cwt.
42 pints milk at 7s. per gallon

If, on this account, a discount of 2% is given, what is the actual amount charged to the nearest penny?

9. $15\frac{1}{2}$ yd. cloth at 11s. 8d. per yd.
9 yd. rayon at 5s. 3d. per yd.
12 yd. cotton at 4s. $5\frac{1}{2}d$. per yd.
$3\frac{3}{4}$ yd. net at 6s. 3d. per yd.

If, on this account, discount is given at the rate of $\frac{1}{2}d$. per 1s., what is the actual amount charged to the nearest penny?

10. The sale of produce from a school allotment is as follows:
2 cwt. early potatoes at $3\frac{1}{2}d$. per lb.
$43\frac{1}{2}$ doz. cabbages at 5s. 9d. per doz.
42 cauliflower at 1s. $1\frac{1}{2}d$. each
25 dozen leeks at $3\frac{1}{4}d$. each

If the cost of production is £8 10s. 5d., what is the profit?

11. 750 nails at 17s. 6d. per thousand
145 ft. lead pipe at 5s. $7\frac{1}{2}d$. per ft.
65 yd. iron wire at 2s. $9\frac{1}{2}d$. per ft.
$3\frac{3}{4}$ gross iron screws at 1s. $10\frac{1}{2}d$. per doz.
19 locks at 5s. 10d. each

Discount at 9d. per £1.

12. $3\frac{1}{2}$ doz. eggs at 5s. 9d. per dozen
$4\frac{3}{4}$ lb. butter at 3s. 10d. per lb.
$4\frac{1}{2}$ pints milk at 4s. 8d. per gallon
$1\frac{1}{2}$ stone sugar at 7d. per lb.
$7\frac{1}{2}$ lb. cheese at £2 15s. per cheese of 25 lb.

Discount at $\frac{3}{4}d$. per 1s.

13. 120 penknives at 3s. 10d. each
    5 doz. chisels at 4s. 1½d. each
    51 spanners at 38s. 8d. per half dozen
    3¾ sq. yd. metal plate at 4s. 8d. per sq. yd.
    1 st. nails at 1s. 7½d. per lb.

Discount at 7½d. per £1.

14. 2 doz. pairs of gloves at 17s. 10½d. per pair
  13¾ yd. velvet at 31s. 9d. per yd.
    1 gross buttons at 5s. 9¾d. per doz.
    6 score studs at 1s. 3¾d. per half dozen
  136 yd. trimming at 7s. 10½d. per dozen yards

Discount at 2½%.

15. Find the cost of a cake made from the following recipe:
    12 oz. butter at 4s. 4d. per lb.
    12 oz. caster sugar at 9d. per lb.
    1½ lb. flour at 8s. 2d. per stone
    6 oz. ground rice at 9d. per lb.
    6 eggs at 5s. 6d. per doz.
    ⅜ pint milk at 6d. per pint

(Give answer to nearest penny.)

(B) Electricity Bills

It is useful to be able to read the electricity meter in your home or later at your place of business. This is comparatively easy if you examine the two types illustrated below. The readings are fairly typical. When the pointer lies between two numbers then the lower number should be read.

Read from left to right

Type A

10,000   1,000   100   10

13*

Type B

10,000   1,000   100   10

Each of the 'clocks' above measures a different amount of electrical energy. For example, the unit on the first one is ten-thousand kilowatt-hours; on the second, thousand kilowatt-hours; on the third, hundred kilowatt-hours, etc.

The kilowatt-hour is the Board of Trade unit of electrical energy and is the work done by a kilowatt ($=1,000$ watts) of electric power acting for one hour.

Suppose we want to read Type A meter.

The reading is $(20,000+3,000+700+80+5)=23,785$ kilowatt-hours.

Similarly, in reading Type B meter,
the reading is $(10,000+7,000+300+80+3)=17,383$ kilowatt-hours.

Normally the electricity meter is read by an Electricity Board official at intervals of six months and the difference between two successive readings gives the amount of electricity consumed in the six-monthly period.

The charge per unit of electricity varies throughout the country and also varies according to the purpose for which it is used. Hence, there are considerable variations in the different tariffs available.

Here are some typical examples.

1. *Domestic Tariff*

     $4\frac{1}{2}d$. for each of the first 15 units per chargeable room
     $1d$. for each additional unit

2. *Farm Tariff*

     $4\frac{1}{2}d$. for each of the first 15 units per chargeable room and for each of the next 100 units
     $1\frac{3}{4}d$. for each of the next 800 units
     $1d$. for each additional unit

3. *General Block Tariff*

     $4\frac{1}{2}d$. for each of the first 100 units
     $1\frac{3}{4}d$. for each additional unit

It will be instructive to consider the following worked examples.

Example 4. Successive electricity meter readings of a six-roomed house are 6,868 and 7,094 units. Find the appropriate bill at domestic tariff rate.

Initial meter reading = 6,868
Final meter reading = 7,094
∴ Number of units consumed = 226
∴ Number of units at $4\frac{1}{2}d$. rate = $15 \times 6 = 90$

∴ Cost of 90 units = £1 13s. 9d.
∴ Number of units at 1d. rate = 136
∴ Cost of 136 units = 11s. 4d.
∴ Total cost of 226 units = £2 5s. 1d.

Example 5. Successive electricity meter readings in a farm-house of 8 apartments are 7,872 and 9,656 units respectively. Find the appropriate bill at farm tariff rate

Initial meter reading = 7,872
Final meter reading = 9,656
∴ Number of units consumed = 1,784
∴ Number of units at $4\frac{1}{2}d$. rate = $15 \times 8 + 100$
= 220

∴ Cost of 220 units = £4 2s. 6d.
Number of units at $1\frac{3}{4}d$. rate = 800
∴ Cost of 800 units = £5 16s. 8d.
Number of units at 1d. rate = 764
∴ Cost of 764 units = £3 3s. 8d.
∴ Total cost of 1,784 units = £13 2s. 10d.

EXERCISE 18B

Make out bills for the electricity used in the following circumstances, using the rates appropriate to the different tariffs.

	Number of Rooms	Initial Meter Reading	Final Meter Reading
General Block Tariff			
1.	—	1,253	1,567
2.	—	2,816	3,024
3.	—	4,928	5,268
4.	—	6,975	7,431
5.	—	7,132	7,686

	Number of Rooms	Initial Meter Reading	Final Meter Reading
Domestic Tariff			
6.	4	5,324	5,486
7.	5	6,583	6,815
8.	6	7,195	7,451
9.	8	9,348	9,692
10.	10	10,681	11,315
Farm Tariff			
11.	4	2,865	3,977
12.	6	3,912	5,234
13.	7	5,434	6,856
14.	9	8,679	10,231
15.	10	11,413	13,017

(C) Gas Bills

It will also be found useful to be able to read the gas meter in your home. This instrument records the number of **hundred** cubic feet of gas consumed and the difference of successive readings will give the quantity of gas used in a given time.

The method of reading the gas meter is very similar to that described for the electricity meter.

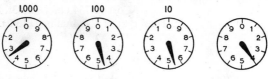

The above gas meter reading is

$(3,000 + 400 + 50 + 4)$ hundred cubic feet $= 345,400$ cubic feet

The gas supplied in any area has a certain calorific (heating) value which may vary for different parts of the country. For example, in one area, 1 cub. ft. of gas may have a calorific value of 425 British Thermal Units (B.Th.U.), whereas in another area the calorific value may be 475 B.Th.U. Normally, the calorific value of 1 cub. ft. of gas lies between 400 and 500 B.Th.U.

Again, frequently in gas bills, the price of gas may be expressed at a certain rate per **therm** where 1 Therm = 100,000 B.Th.U. Hence it

becomes necessary to convert cubic feet to therms in the following way:

1. Multiply the number of cubic feet used by the calorific value and 2. Divide the result by 100,000.

Example 6. Successive gas meter readings are 3,454 and 3,562 in an area where the calorific value of 1 cub. ft. of gas is 450. Calculate how many therms are consumed.

$$\text{Initial meter reading} = 3,454$$
$$\text{Final meter reading} = 3,562$$
$$\therefore \text{Number of cub. ft. of gas consumed} = 108 \times 100$$

But 1 cub. ft. of gas $\equiv$ 450 B.Th.U.

$$\therefore \text{Number of therms consumed} = \frac{108 \times 100 \times 450}{100,000}$$

$$= \frac{243}{5}$$

$$= 48 \cdot 6$$

Here, too, there are various ways in which the cost of gas may be reckoned, but we will consider only two.

1. Tariff System

	Tariff Numbers						
	1	2	3	4	5	6	10
Therms	Price per Therm in Pence						
First 30	17·5	18·5	19·5	20·0	21·5	22	24·5
Next 600	15·5	16·5	17·5	18·0	19·5	20	21·5
Next 600	14·5	15·5	16·5	17·0	18·5	19	20·5

Under this system, the consumer is given a certain tariff number ...ding on the number of gas appliances used. On the basis of ...iff number ... s per therm is determined.

2. Domestic Two-Part Tariff System

In this case the consumer is charged

(*a*) for all gas consumed at a certain rate per therm
plus (*b*) a standing charge per quarter determined by the number of
apartments in the house.

For example, in a certain area the following are the charges under
this system:

(*a*) 11·5*d*. per therm for all gas consumed plus standing charge for
(*b*) (i) house of up to 3 apartments—17*s*. 6*d*. per quarter
     (ii) house of 4 to 6 apartments —20*s*. per quarter
     (iii) house of over 6 apartments —22*s*. 6*d*. per quarter

Example 7. The successive gas meter readings in a house with
tariff number 3 are 5,818 and 5,954. Find the cost assuming the
calorific value of 1 cub. ft. = 425 B.ThU.

$$\text{Initial meter reading} = 5,818$$
$$\text{Final meter reading} = 5,954$$

∴ Number of cub. ft. of gas consumed $= 136 \times 100$

But 1 cub. ft. ≡ 425 B.Th.U.

∴ Number of therms of gas consumed $= \dfrac{\overset{34}{\cancel{136}} \times \cancel{100} \times \overset{\overset{17}{\cancel{85}}}{\cancel{425}}}{\underset{\underset{\underset{10}{40}}{200}}{100,000}} = 57\cdot8$

Under tariff number 3,

cost of first 30 therms $= 19\cdot5d. \times 30 = 585d.$
$$= £2\ 8s.\ 9d.$$

and cost of remaining 27·8 therms $= 17\cdot5d. \times 27\cdot8 = 486\cdot5d.$
$$= £2\ 0s.\ 6\tfrac{1}{2}d.$$

∴ Gas bill $= £4\ 9s.\ 4d.$

(to necessary penny)

Example 8. In a 5-apartment house the gas meter readings at the
beginning and end of a certain quarter are 6,432 and 6,576 respectively. Find the gas bill assuming 1 cub. ft. ≡ 450 B.Th.U., co⸱
1 therm = 11·5*d*. and charge is made under two-part tariff sy⸱

Initial meter reading = 6,432

Final meter reading = 6,576

∴ Number of cub. ft. of gas consumed = 144×100

But 1 cub. ft. ≡ 450 B.Th.U.

∴ Number of therms of gas consumed = $\dfrac{\overset{36}{\cancel{144}} \times \overset{9}{\cancel{100}} \times \overset{}{\cancel{450}}}{\underset{\underset{5}{20}}{100,000}} = 60.8$

But 1 therm of gas costs 11·5d.

∴ 60·8 therms of gas cost 11·5d. × 60·8 = £2 18s. 4d.

(to necessary penny)

And rental per quarter = £1

∴ Total gas bill = £3 18s. 4d.

EXERCISE 18c

Make out quarterly gas bills in the following circumstances to the appropriate penny.

Tariff System

	Tariff Number	Number of Therms		Tariff Number	Number of Therms
1.	2	24	2.	3	196
3.	5	345	4.	6	752
5.	10	931			

Two-Part Tariff System

	Number of Rooms	Number of Therms		Number of Rooms	Number of Therms
6.	3	96	7.	5	122
8.	6	143	9.	8	191
10.	9	253			

Tariff System

	Tariff Number	Initial Meter Reading (100 cub. ft.)	Final Meter Reading (100 cub. ft.)	Number of B.Th.U./Cub. ft.
11.	1	2,315	2,351	425
12.	3	3,564	3,616	425
13.	4	4,739	4,821	450
14.	5	5,843	6,125	450
5.	6	1	7,367	475

Two-Part Tariff System

	Number of Rooms	Initial Meter Reading (100 cub. ft.)	Final Meter Reading (100 cub. ft.)	Number of B.Th.U/Cub. ft.
16.	2	3,426	3,472	425
17.	4	4,675	4,763	430
18.	5	5,841	6,215	435
19.	7	6,954	7,648	450
20.	10	8,252	9,478	475

Exercise 18d

1. Calculate the following gas bill correct to the nearest penny: 1st meter reading—19,800 cub. ft.; 2nd meter reading—26,300 cub. ft., when 1,000 cub. ft. yields 4·7 therms and the price per therm is 8·925d.

2. A gas fire burns 1 cub. ft. of gas in 66 sec. If 1,000 cub. ft. of gas give 4·5 therms and the charge is 11·55d. per therm, find, to the nearest penny, the cost per hour of burning the gas fire.

3. A gas meter reads 234,500 cub. ft. at the beginning and 288,300 cub. ft. at the end of the quarter. 1,000 cub. ft. of gas are equivalent to 4·75 therms, and the price of gas is 10d. per therm. What is the cost to the consumer, to the nearest penny, when a discount of $2\frac{1}{2}\%$ is allowed for prompt payment?

4. In a certain town, the price of gas is 10·4d. per therm. One therm is equivalent to 100,000 heat units and 1 cub. ft. of gas will give out 450 of the latter. If the consumer's bill is £11 14s., how many cubic feet of gas have been burned?

5. A householder's bills for electricity and gas read as follows:
Electricity: 64 units at $4\frac{1}{2}d.$ per unit
            576 units at 0·75d. per unit
            300 units at 0·55d. per unit
Gas: 3,700 cub. ft. at 1s. $1\frac{1}{2}d.$ per therm
Calculate, to the necessary penny, the total amount payable. (100,000 cub. ft. of gas produce 450 therms.)

6. Find the weekly cost of burning a gas fire 6 hours a day, if the fire consumes 50 cub. ft. per hour and gas is 11d. per therm, each therm being equivalent to 220 cub. ft.

If an electric fire in another room burns each day 2 units per hour for 2 hours and 1 unit per hour for 4 hours, find which fire is cheaper, and find the difference in cost per week, electricity costing $3\frac{1}{2}d.$ per unit for heating.

7. An electric supply company charges a consumer who lives in a house with x-apartments as follows: the first $8x$ units are charged at $4d.$ per unit, the next $72x$ units at $0.65d.$ per unit and all additional units at $0.45d.$ per unit.

   (i) Find how much the account is when 630 units are used in a 4-apartment house

  (ii) If the account in the case of a 5-apartment house is £2 4s. 10d., how many units have been used?

8. Electric power may be paid for either

  (i) at the rate of $2\frac{1}{4}d.$ per unit for heating and $4\frac{1}{2}d.$ per unit for lighting,

or (ii) at a fixed quarterly charge of £1 5s. together with a charge of $1\frac{1}{4}d.$ per unit for all electricity.

If the quarterly consumption is 261 units for lighting and 94 for heating, find the cheaper method of payment and by how much it is cheaper.

9. In a certain district, electric current may be paid for either (i) by a fixed meter rent of 12s. a year together with 8d. per unit used *or* (ii) by a fixed yearly charge of 20% of the rateable value of the house together with a charge of $1\frac{1}{2}d.$ per unit used. In a certain house of rateable value £34 the yearly consumption was 156 units. Find the payment due per annum under each of these two systems.

10. Electric current may be paid for (i) at the rate of $4\frac{1}{2}d.$ per unit for lighting and 2d. per unit if used for heating, *or* (ii) at a fixed yearly charge of 14% of the rateable value of the house together with $1\frac{1}{4}d.$ per unit used for either purpose. A householder uses in a year 190 units of current for lighting and 950 units for heating and the rateable value of his house is £35. What method of payment will be the more economical, and by how much?

TABLES

Capacity

LIQUID MEASURE

4 gills	=	1 pint (pt)
2 pints	=	1 quart (qt)
4 quarts	=	1 gallon (gall)

DRY MEASURE

2 gallons	=	1 peck (pk)
4 pecks	=	1 bushel (bush)
8 bushels	=	1 quarter (qr)

1 litre = 1 cu dm = 1000 cu cm

10 centilitres (cl)	=	1 decilitre (dl)
10 decilitres	=	1 litre (l)
10 litres	=	1 Dekalitre (Dl)

APPROXIMATE EQUIVALENTS

1 gallon	=	277·3 cu in	=	4·546 litres
1 cu ft	=	6·23 gall	=	28·326 litres
1 litre	=	61·03 cu in	=	1·76 pints (1¾ pints)

Weight

16 ounces (oz)	=	1 pound (lb)		10 milligrams (mg)	=	1 centigram (cg)
14 pounds	=	1 stone (st)		10 centigrams	=	1 decigram (dg)
8 stones	=	1 hundredweight (cwt)		10 decigrams	=	1 gram (g)
20 cwt	=	1 ton		10 grams	=	1 Dekagram (Dg)
				10 Dekagrams	=	1 Hectogram (Hg)
28 pounds	=	1 quarter (qr)		10 Hectograms	=	1 Kilogram (Kg)
4 quarters	=	1 cwt				
112 pounds	=	1 cwt		100 Kilograms	=	1 Quintal
2240 pounds	=	1 ton		1000 Kilograms	=	1 metric ton

E 4

COUNTY COUNCIL OF THE COUNTY OF LANARK
EDUCATION COMMITTEE

Lesmahgow .... School.

(1) This book is the property of the Education Authority, and is intended for the use of scholars attending Schools in the County of Lanark.

(2) Parents and Guardians are asked to co-operate with the Teachers in seeing that the Book is kept clean and in good repair.

(3) When a leaf becomes loose or gets torn, it should at once be shown to the Teacher of the class.

(4) The Parent or Guardian of a scholar losing or misusing a book will be required to replace it, or to refund to the Education Authority the value of the book.

(5) The book must be covered by the pupil to whom it is issued.

Date	Name	Class
29/8/...	Janette Brown	IIIA
29/8/61	Rae Muir	IB
24 Aug 62	Archie Mackenzie	IIA
	Elizabeth Gibb	IA
26/8/64	Elizabeth Gibb	IIA

TABLES

Area

144 sq inches	= 1 sq foot		100 sq mm	= 1 sq cm
9 sq feet	= 1 sq yard		100 sq cm	= 1 sq dm
484 sq yd	= 1 sq chain		100 sq dm	= 1 sq m
10 sq ch	= 1 acre (ac)		100 sq m	= 1 sq Dm (1 are)
640 acres	= 1 sq mile		100 sq Dm	= 1 sq Hm
			100 sq Hm	= 1 sq Km

4840 sq yd = 1 acre

APPROXIMATE EQUIVALENTS

1 sq in = 6·4516 sq cm

1 sq cm = 0·1550 sq in

Volume

1728 cu in	= 1 cu ft		1000 cu mm	= 1 cu cm
27 cu ft	= 1 cu yd		1000 cu cm	= 1 cu dm = 1 litre
			1000 cu dm	= 1 cu m
			1000 cu m	= 1 cu Dm
1 cu in	= 16·387 cu cm		1000 cu Dm	= 1 cu Hm
1 cu cm	= 0·061024 cu in		1000 cu Hm	= 1 cu Km